T02615

TROPICAL
WILD FLOWERS

by

V. E. GRAHAM, B.Sc.

*with drawings by the author of nearly 300 plants,
32 in full colour*

HULTON EDUCATIONAL PUBLICATIONS

CONTENTS

©
V. E. GRAHAM
1963

First Published 1963 by Hulton Educational Publications Ltd.,
55/59 Saffron Hill, London, E.C.1.

Printed by Cox and Wyman Ltd., London, Reading and Fakenham

581.9093

INTRODUCTION

It is hoped that this book will help the average person to name many of the common wild flowers of his area. Owing to the vast number of different tropical flowering plants, it has been impossible to include flowering trees, except a few which flower when they are quite small. This means that many families which contain only woody plants, together with those very poorly represented in the tropics, have been omitted altogether. It has also been decided, owing to their large number, and difficulty of identification by any except an expert, to omit all grasses and orchids. There are, however, comprehensive books on these two families which can be consulted by those who wish to study them.

It is not easy to devise a book which the ordinary reader can use to identify the tropical flowers of a large area. Botanical Keys require some technical knowledge, and are of very limited use to a person with little acquaintance with Botany. Keys, therefore, are not used here and the plan has been to rely on short descriptions with drawings. Nearly all of the almost three hundred genera described are illustrated by typical species drawn by the author from living plants. As the species and sub-species are very numerous, the reader should be satisfied if he is able to place his specimens in their correct genera, or maybe in the correct family. Once this has been done it is often possible to run down the exact species in an herbarium. There is often an herbarium at the local Agricultural Department, or at the Forestry Departments. Many tropical wild flowers have no common names. For this reason the International or Scientific names have been used throughout in this book. Where no common name is given, the reader might like to insert any local name he knows after the International name.

From the botanical point of view the tropics can be divided

into distinct regions in which the native plants show little over-lapping. Some whole families, for instance, are peculiar to South America, others to Africa, or Asia. Only a few of the members of these families can be included here. There are, however, many wild flowers, mostly weeds of cultivation, or plants which have been naturalized by accident or design which occur in practically all hot countries. These plants form the bulk of those mentioned in this book, for they are the plants most likely to be met with by the reader.

While the non-botanist can probably match many plants from the illustrations, which are drawn approximately two-thirds natural size, all specimens should, of course, be examined with care, preferably with a hand lens, before deciding on their identification. Many flowers look superficially very much alike, and easily mislead the unwary. It is best to get some idea of how plants are actually classified, and a chapter on this subject follows this introduction.

Scientific terms have been reduced to a minimum, but some are obviously necessary. Most of those used in this volume are explained in the chapter on classification, or where they occur in the text, but for convenience a short glossary of these is placed after the systematic list of plants and their illustrations.

The common plants of most tropical countries have not been sufficiently studied. This is a piece of work open to any inter-ested person, whether he has specialized knowledge or not, and a valuable project for schools. If the reader likes to collect and name the plants of his area he will find the subject of absorbing interest. Some hints are included in an appendix at the end.

My thanks are due to everyone who has helped me to visit the places where the flowers were found, to the Director and Staff of the herbarium at Kew Gardens, who determined more than five hundred of my specimens, and to Mr. S. G. Harrison, Keeper of the Botany Department of the National Museum of Wales, who kindly read and corrected the proofs.

V.G.

4

THE CLASSIFICATION OF FLOWERING PLANTS

Scientists base their classification of plants on the assumption that they all have a common origin, and are therefore related to one another. The nearer the relationship, the more characteristics they will show in common, especially those connected with the flower structure. Owing to the fact that plants living in very similar situations often develop very similar vegetative characters, the shapes of the stems, roots and leaves are a less sure guide to relationship than is the flower structure.

Under the present system, every plant has two International, or Scientific names. This binomial system of naming is due to the famous Swedish botanist Linnaeus (1708–78). Many of his original names are still used, but others have been altered as further knowledge has exposed different relationships. Every plant illustrated in this book therefore has two Scientific names, and no two different plants have the same Scientific name, anywhere in the world.

Flowering plants are all included in one great group, known as the *Seed Plants* (*Spermaphyta*). The fact that they can produce seeds distinguishes them from all lower plants such as ferns and seaweeds. If we find a 'fern' with flowers or seeds, then it is obviously mis-named, because it is not really a fern. No ferns are included in this book. Seed Plants are again divided into those which produce their seeds in some kind of fruit, nut, pod, capsule etc: the *Angiosperms* (Greek: Covered Seeds) and those which produce naked seeds in cones: the *Gymnosperms* (Greek: Naked Seeds). Only Angiosperms are included in this book, as most of the Gymnosperms are trees, and they nearly all live in the Temperate Regions.

The Angiosperms are again divided into two large *Classes* according to the form of the seedling and the positions of the conducting vessels in their stems and leaves: *Monocotyledons* (Greek: One Seed Leaf) and *Dicotyledons* (Greek: Two Seed

Leaves). From our point of view the easiest way of distinguishing these two classes is by looking at their leaves. With few exceptions, the Monocotyledons have their leaf veins running side by side with few cross connections, whereas in Dicotyledons the veins are much branched (net-veined). The Monocotyledon plants are here placed after the Dicotyledons, because it appears that they are in some ways more highly specialized.

The next grouping is into *Orders* and *Families* of plants which are more and more alike. In this book the name and the characteristics of the Family will be given for each example or series of examples. Finally we come to the Scientific names mentioned above, borne by each plant. The first name indicates the *Genus*. Each family has one or more *Genera* which we can compare with our surnames or family names. While all the members of a genus are recognizably very much alike, they each show certain characteristics which mark them off as distinct kinds of plants, or different *Species*. The second name of every plant is its *Specific* epithet, and applies to all the individuals of that particular kind of plant.

Let us take some examples. Most people are well acquainted with the cultivated ornamental Hibiscus plant. An examination of Ochro, commonly grown as a vegetable for its fleshy seed pods, shows a flower structure which is practically identical with that of the ornamental Hibiscus. Both are, in fact, members of the Genus *Hibiscus* but the smaller details in which they differ mark them off as separate Species. The Scientific name of the common ornamental Hibiscus is *Hibiscus rosa-sinensis*. That of Ochro is *Hibiscus esculentus*. (Note that the name of the genus always begins with a capital letter, but the species epithet always begins with a small letter. Old-fashioned authors use a capital initial letter when the epithet is derived from a proper noun.)

Cotton often grows wild. If we examine the flowers of this plant we find they are strikingly like *Hibiscus*, but the seed pod and seeds differ, the seeds bearing the long white hairs which form the well-known fibre cotton. This, and some other details of structure, make the plant different enough to belong to a

6

different genus, *Gossypium*; the two genera *Hibiscus* and *Gossypium*, together with others, are included in the Family *Malvaceae*, and an examination of the leaves of a plant of either genus will quickly decide that they are both members of the Class *Dicotyledons*. We can now make out a 'family tree' for these plants:

Class: *Dicotyledons*
Order: *Malvales* (several families are included in one Order)
Family: *Malvaceae*
Genus: *Hibiscus*, or *Gossypium*, etc.
Species: *rosa-sinensis*, etc.

How is this kind of classification arrived at? In most cases by an examination of the flower structure. This usually requires a hand lens, and detailed structure in some very small flowers can only be seen by using a microscope. However, most plants can be identified by using a hand lens.

The structure of a flower

The essential parts of a flower are not, as one might suppose, the showy petals and sepals, the leaf-like parts which make the greater part of most flowers, but the usually insignificant central part, consisting of male organs (*Stamens*) and female organs (*Carpels*). Most flowers have both stamens and carpels, but a large number have only one of these two types of organs, so that they can be thought of as 'male' if they have stamens only, or 'female' if they have carpels only.

The chief parts of a flower are described below, and the novice is advised to examine a large simple flower as he reads the description, referring to the diagram where necessary until he is familiar with the number and arrangement of the different parts, and repeating the exercise with other and more complicated flowers to gain practice.

Sepals. The outermost, usually green, floral leaves are often the only parts visible in the bud. They form a whorl, or are arranged spirally. (Do not confuse them with leaves immediately *below* the flower (*Bracts* and *Bracteoles*) which may even be coloured.) Collectively the sepals form the *Calyx*. They may be joined together, and are sometimes absent.

7

Petals. The usually showy floral leaves just inside the calyx. They may be free or joined, and other parts, such as stamens, may be joined to them. In some flowers they are absent altogether. Collectively they are termed the *Corolla*. The word *Perianth* may be used to describe the petals and sepals, especially if either whorl is missing, or if they are both alike.

Stamens. These are the male organs. They are thought to be very much altered leaves. In fact, in some flowers they are 'petaloid' and not functional. The inner petals merge with petaloid stamens in Water Lily (*Nymphaea*). In *Canna*, and Ginger Lily (*Hedychium*) most of the stamens have become petaloid. In other cases the stamens bear curious outgrowths, or some may be functionless remnants called *Staminodes*. Typical Stamens have slender stalks or *Filaments* bearing *Anthers* at the top. Inside the anthers, *Pollen* is produced.

Carpels. Like male organs, the female organs are considered to be much altered leaves. In this case it is supposed that the *Ovules* which contain the egg cells were originally borne on the margin of a green leaf, as they still are in some Gymnosperms. This green leaf has been turned in on itself in flowering plants and joined up to make a hollow box, the *Ovary*, surmounted by a *Stigma* to receive pollen. The part between ovary and stigma is usually elongated to form a *Style*. A complete flower may have one carpel, as in the various peas and beans, and in mango, or several carpels, which in most plants are united to make a single ovary, but are quite separate in Lotus Lily (*Nelumbium*) and some other flowers. The number and arrangement of the carpels is especially important in classification.

All the various floral parts are borne at the end of a special stem, which is swollen out to hold them. The swollen part, *Receptacle* or *Torus*, may be raised or flat, or hollow. In many plants it is so hollowed out that the ovary is completely enclosed by it, and is said to be *inferior*; in its normal position the ovary comes at the top of the floral axis, so that it is *superior*. In a few families the receptacle surrounds the ovary like a cup, and the flower is then *perigynous*.

8

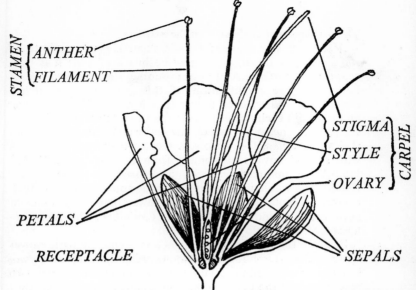

STAMEN { ANTHER, FILAMENT }

STIGMA, STYLE, OVARY } CARPEL

PETALS

RECEPTACLE

SEPALS

THE FLOWER PARTS IN A HALF-FLOWER OF CÆSALPINIA

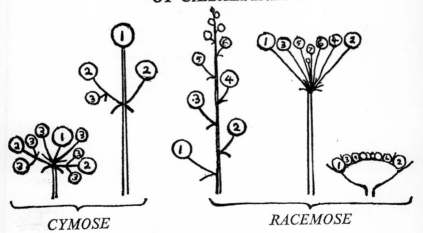

CYMOSE

RACEMOSE

SOME INFLORESCENCES

The arrangement of flowers on the plant

A single flower may end a main stem. Then it is said to be *solitary and terminal*. Or it may be in a leaf axil; it is then *solitary and axillary*. All flower groupings or *inflorescences* are built on some modification of this pattern. A branched inflorescence where each flower ends a main stem is a *Cyme*, and one with each flower in a leaf axil or a lateral position is a *Raceme*. A raceme in which the individual flowers have no stalks is a *Spike*. Conversely, a raceme truncated at the end with stalked flowers all coming from the top is an *Umbel*. Umbel-like inflorescences can also originate from cymes. Finally, the whole inflorescence may be condensed on a much enlarged receptacle, the individual flowers having no stalks at all, forming a kind of head called a *Capitulum*. This is characteristic of the Sunflower family.

Each of the families of flowers has a characteristic flower structure. In this book the families with the simplest flower structure are placed first. Those with no perianth might not be recognized by the ordinary person as flowers at all, but they have the essential male and female parts, so they really are flowers, and can immediately be recognized as such by anyone with a little experience. The novice often confuses the bract leaves, associated with flowers, and often brightly coloured, with true flowers, but a more careful examination will soon point out the mistake. The variety of form in tropical flowers is endless, and will delight the interested student.

FLOWERS OF DICOTYLEDON FAMILIES

Two Seed Leaves

Leaf veins form a network

Flower parts often in twos or fives

Veins in the stem form a ring in cross section

PIPERACEAE. This is the family to which the true 'black' or 'white' Pepper belongs. 'Red' Pepper belongs to another family, which comes later in this book.

In *Piperaceae* the flowers are in close spikes, and very small. They have no perianth, and the male and female flowers are separate. The plants are herbs or shrubs, some of them climbing by roots on the stem, as in the cultivated Pepper. The leaves are often palmately net-veined and may have a biting taste. They are always arranged alternately. There are seven genera, the two most important being *Piper* and *Peperomia*.

Piper. In this genus the leaves have sheathing stipules, and the plants are shrubby. *Piper obliquum*, Cow's Hoof (illustrated), is a common weed in many parts of the tropics, which generally turns up on cultivated ground. It has large, beautifully veined, heart-shaped leaves, and clusters of whitish flower spikes. It grows to four feet or more, generally in shady places.

About seven hundred species of *Piper* are known, including the cultivated Pepper (*P. nigrum* and others). The fleshy fruit of this plant is collected and dried, forming black pepper. If the skin of the fruit is removed before drying, it is white pepper.

Peperomia. This is a genus of rather fleshy herbs with watery juice, some species growing on the ground, and others on trees. In some species the leaves are prettily marked, and they are in demand as house plants. The leaves bear no stipules.

Peperomia pellucida, Shiny Bush (illustrated), is a common weed on damp ground in shady places in most parts of the tropics. It is a small herb with delicate watery leaves which are heart-shaped and very glossy above. It grows from a few inches to nearly a foot tall, and comes rapidly from seed, completing its life history in a few weeks. In the West Indies it is credited with various medicinal properties, and the leaves are certainly pleasant to eat in a green salad.

BATIDACEAE. This curious family is founded on the single genus and single species illustrated, the Salt Bush, *Batis maritima*. This is a small shrub or semi-trailing plant with fleshy, opposite, yellowish green leaves, which grows on coastal strands and mud flats in many parts of the tropics. All its parts

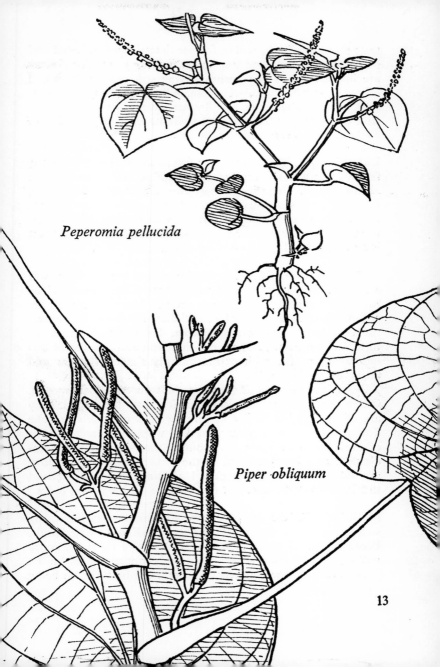

Peperomia pellucida

Piper obliquum

13

taste strongly of salt, and in former times it was collected and burnt to yield soda and potash for making glass. The flowers are insignificant, some bushes having stiff male catkins and others having fleshy spikes of female flowers with their ovaries sunk in the fleshy tissue. The flowers have no perianth. As the fruit develops, the fleshy female spike becomes dry and full of air spaces. It is dispersed by the sea.

LAURACEAE. This is mainly a family of trees, including the famous South American Greenheart and Avocado Pear, as well as Cinnamon. There is one herb, a peculiar leafless parasite, *Cassytha filiformis* (illustrated). It has orange or yellow stems and minute greenish white flowers with six perianth leaves, followed by a white or pink berry with a single seed. This plant is an agricultural pest in some parts of the tropics.

ARISTOLOCHIACEAE. A family of twining climbers with alternate, often lobed, leaves, without stipules or tendrils. The roots are medicinal. The flowers are of interest, as they are pollinated in a special way by small flies. There are five genera, the best known being **Aristolochia,** Birthwort, Dutchman's Pipe, Pelican Flower. There are three hundred species of this interesting genus, with extraordinarily shaped flowers and attractive seed capsules.

Aristolochia consimilis (illustrated) is an American species. Others are found in open bushy places all over the tropics. They are often found climbing in forest glades or by rivers. The flowers are creamish yellow, marked with checkered patterns of dark maroon. They are tubular, the perianth being undivided, and being hooded at the top, and enlarged below, around the stamens and carpels. Hairs lining the tube can bend to allow insects to enter but not to leave till the flower fades.

MORACEAE. The Mulberry and Fig family contains many well-known trees of tropical regions, including the Bread-fruit, Bread Nut, Jack Fruit and Banyan. Most of them contain a milky juice; in some genera the tree is tapped for its 'milk'. There are very few herbaceous genera, the best known being

14

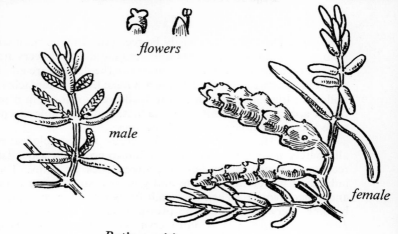

flowers

male

female

Batis maritima

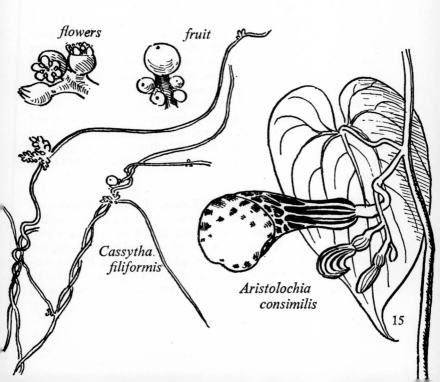

flowers

fruit

Cassytha filiformis

Aristolochia consimilis

15

Dorstenia. The family can easily be recognized by its peculiar inflorescence, in which a large number of stalkless flowers are massed on a fleshy receptacle. Sometimes the flowers are all of one sex; in other cases the flowers are mixed. The receptacle is hollow in Figs and Banyans, with the flowers enclosed in it so that it appears like a fruit from the first, and the whole receptacle becomes edible when the fruit ripens.

Dorstenia. Herbs, or occasionally shrubs, with simple leaves alternately arranged, and curious inflorescences on a wide, flat receptacle which often has spreading lobes or arms. The individual flowers are minute and greenish, some being male and others female. When the small fruits ripen the receptacle becomes very turgid and the pressure pushes the seeds out. *Dorstenia contrayerva*, Contrayerva Root (illustrated), is a West Indian species supposed to have medicinal properties.

URTICACEAE. This is the family to which true nettles belong. Various nettles are found all over the world. Most of them are herbaceous, some of them being pernicious weeds with creeping rhizomes. Others are tropical trees. Many of them have stinging gland hairs on their leaves and stems. The young leaves of some, when cooked, are edible. Many members of the family yield fibres in the stems, the best known being Ramie fibre (*Boehmeria nivea*), grown mainly in China.

Fleurya. A genus of annual tropical nettles with toothed, long-stemmed leaves and axillary clusters of greenish male and female flowers on erect, ridged stems. Most species have stinging hairs. *Fleurya aestuans* (illustrated) is a common species found on waste land all over the tropics. It grows from one to three feet tall.

POLYGONACEAE. This is a family of mostly herbaceous plants, with simple, alternately arranged leaves, usually with a peculiar papery sheath at the base, called an *ochrea*, which clasps the stem. A few are trees of tropical regions, as, for example, the Seaside Grape (*Coccoloba*) of West Indian seashores, and the Christmas Candle Tree (*Triplaris*) of South America. They have panicles of small, simple flowers, with

16

*Fleurya
aestuans*

*Dorstenia
contrayerva*

17

petals and sepals alike, usually green or white, but sometimes pink. There are usually three united carpels, which produce a nut or a drupe. Very often the perianth grows with the fruit, and provides a winged structure for wind dispersal. Very few plants of this family are of use to man. Buckwheat (*Fagopyrum*) is grown for its edible seeds, and Rhubarb (*Rheum*) has edible leaf stalks and a root of medicinal value. Most of the family are pernicious weeds, especially in the temperate regions. The three genera mentioned below are found in most tropical countries, the last mentioned often being a garden escape on waste land.

Symmeria. A genus of shrubby plants common in many parts of West Africa and South America, in open bushy places. The flowers are small, clustered in branched spikes, with numerous stamens. The nuts are three-sided, surrounded by the persistent perianth. *Symmeria paniculata* (illustrated) has creamish yellow flowers. It is found in West Africa, British Guiana and Brazil. It is usually a small shrub, but may grow into a small tree.

Polygonum. A genus of herbs, often of wet places, with pink or white flowers in close spikes, and leaves with a well-marked tubular ochrea at the base, and often bristles above it. The small nuts are smooth and shining, not triangular. *Polygonum punctatum* (illustrated) and other closely related species are common semi-aquatic plants in rice fields and the margins of drainage trenches, which spread over the surface of the water or on dried up mud. The flowers are pinkish white.

Antigonon. A genus of rampant perennial climbers with pretty pink or white flowers and heart-shaped pointed leaves. The axillary branches form branched tendrils, often bearing the inflorescence as well. The fruit is a triangular nut in a persistent winged perianth. *Antigonon leptopus*, Corallita, (illustrated) is a native of Central America.

AMARANTACEAE. This is mainly a family of the tropics and sub-tropics, where it replaces a very common family of the temperate regions, *Chenopodiaceae*, or the Spinach family. Under the name of 'Spinach' or 'Callalou', many of the

18

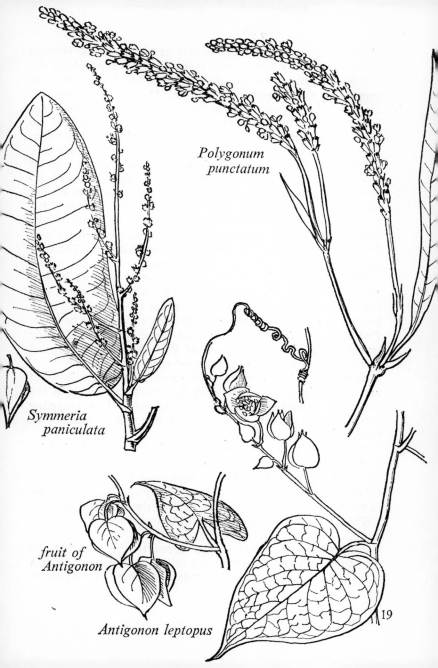

Polygonum punctatum

Symmeria paniculata

fruit of Antigonon

Antigonon leptopus

19

Amarantaceae are also eaten as pot herbs. It may be because of this that many have spread to waste places throughout the tropics. Nearly all the genera are herbs, weeds of cultivated ground or salty places near the sea. They have opposite or alternate simple leaves without stipules, and small, insignificant flowers in branched inflorescences. Below the flowers are bracts, often scale-like, and these may be coloured. The upper leaves are also coloured in some species of *Amaranthus*. Species of this genus, Prince's Feather, of *Celosia* and of *Gomphrena*, Bachelor's Buttons, all have gaily coloured inflorescences and are often grown in flower gardens, from whence they may escape and become naturalized. In this family the flowers are regular with one series of perianth leaves, usually regarded as sepals, because the stamens are opposite them. The stamens are united at the base by their filaments. The fruit may be dry and nut-like or a little capsule.

Philoxerus. This is a genus of small fleshy plants with low spreading habit. The fleshy, oblong leaves are opposite, and the flowers are in short spikes or heads at the ends of the main branches. Each flower has a whitish scale-like bract beneath. *Philoxerus vermicularis* (illustrated) is a common plant of sandy or muddy tropical shores both of West Africa and Tropical America. It is a creeping plant rooting at the nodes.

Telanthera. Many species of this genus resemble the last, but are distinguished by the whitish flower-clusters being in the leaf axils. *Telanthera polygonoides* (illustrated) is a straggling weed of waste ground, with smooth leaves and swollen nodes, from which numerous roots arise.

Pupalia. A genus of erect herbs a foot or more in height, with spikes of flowers in close clusters, and opposite leaves. Some of the flowers are barren, and these carry four hooked spines. When the fruit ripens, clusters are pulled off by catching in the coats of passing animals, and so the seed is dispersed. *Pupalia lappacea* (illustrated) is widely distributed on waste land.

Achyranthes. A rather similar genus to the last, but the minute flowers are in simple erect spikes, each flower having a scale-like bract beneath, which ends in a spine. As the flowers

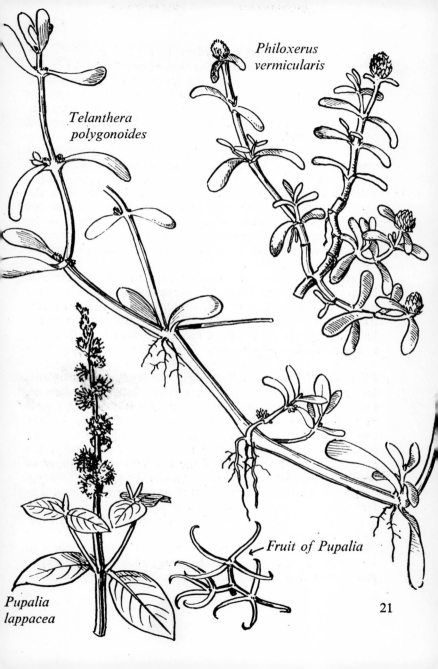

Philoxerus vermicularis

Telanthera polygonoides

Pupalia lappacea

Fruit of Pupalia

21

mature, they bend over and, when the fruit ripens, the sharp spines of the bracts catch in the skin of passers-by, or in the coats of animals. *Achyranthes aspera*, Devil's Whip(illustrated), is a common perennial weed of waste ground throughout the tropics. Both stem and leaves bear silky hairs. This plant has established itself far and wide because of its effective method of seed dispersal.

Amaranthus. There are many species of this genus which grow on cultivated land, roadsides and rubbish heaps all over the tropics and sub-tropics. One common species, *Amaranthus spinosa*, bears spines in the leaf axils. Others, such as the species illustrated (*Amaranthus gracilis*), make good substitutes for spinach. This genus is distinguished from the next by the bracts beneath the flowers, by their perianths being leafy, not papery or scaly, and by the fruit being an achene (like a minute nut). Most are annuals.

Celosia. This genus of annual herbs has erect inflorescences in which the bracts and perianths are satiny scales. In some they are pink or yellow, in others, white. *Celosia argentea* (illustrated) is a common annual weed in Africa which has silvery bracts. It is also found in the far East, which is probably its native habitat.

PHYTOLACCACEAE. A family of mostly herbaceous plants looking to the casual observer very like the last, but the flowers, though small, are larger, the inflorescence is usually a simple raceme, the stamens are not joined at their bases, and the leaves are never opposite. The fruit is often fleshy (a berry). Some members of the family are climbers, and a few are shrubs. Like the members of the last family, a number of species are used as green vegetables under the name of 'Spinach' or 'Callalou'. Others are collected as native medicines. The family is of little economic value.

Phytolacca, Deer Callalou. Both African and American species of this genus are found. They may be erect annual herbs or climbers. Their leaves are hairless and simple. The flowers, in simple racemes, have five or more rounded perianth leaves, which may be coloured or greenish. These are followed by

22

Achyranthes aspera

Celosia argentea

Petiveria alliacea

Amaranthus gracilis

23

fleshy fruits, which in some species are red, blue or purplish. The stems and fruit stalks are often bright crimson or purple. *Phytolacca icosandra*, Deer Callalou (illustrated), is a South American species which characteristically springs up when bush is cleared and is grazed by deer and other animals. The flowers are pale pink, and the button-shaped fruits are green, their stalks being crimson.

Microtea. This genus resembles the last, but the fruit is nut-like, not fleshy, and the flowers are smaller. *Microtea debilis* (illustrated) is a weed of cultivated ground, especially in the West Indies. It can be used as a pot herb. It has a low, straggling habit, and hairless leaves and stems. The flowers are white.

Petiveria. There are two species of this West Indian genus, which has spikes of insignificant star-shaped flowers and small dry fruits. *Petiveria alliacea*, Gully Root (illustrated), is a perennial weed of shady places under trees. Its underground parts are used by West Indians medicinally. It is a plant a foot or more in height with erect spikes of small pinkish flowers, each perianth leaf having a green line down the middle. This plant has been naturalized in several tropical countries.

Rivina. This is a genus of rather pretty slender perennial herbs native to South America. There are four species, which bear racemes of flowers with parts in fours, followed by fleshy fruits. *Rivina brasiliensis* (illustrated) is an erect plant less than a foot tall, with white flowers followed by bright scarlet fruits. The perianth leaves are bent back in fruit. It now grows wild in many tropical places, generally in the shade under hedges.

CARYOPHYLLACEAE is the family to which the garden Carnation belongs. Though not native to the tropics, these flowers are grown in many tropical gardens for their scented flowers. The family is recognized by its jointed stems with opposite leaves, and very regular flowers with superior ovaries, arranged in cymes. The leaves have no stipules as a rule; a few genera have bristles. The petals are free, and the stamens are double the number of the petals. Nearly all the members of the family are herbs, often weeds of cultivated land, or ephemeral plants of dry savannahs and sandy or rocky places. The flowers

*Rivina
brasiliensis*

*Microtea
debilis*

*Phytolacca
icosandra*

25

are white or pink, sometimes unisexual, and are followed by capsules which open by valves or teeth at the apex. The seeds are arranged on a raised lump at the base of the capsule, which has no partitions. The seeds are usually round with an indentation (cochleate) and spread by the wind.

Drymaria. A genus of weak straggling herbs with broad leaves and slender stems which run along the ground. The leaves have divided stipules on the joints between each pair. The ovary is made of three carpels, and has three styles, joined at the base and the filaments of the stamens are joined at the base. *Drymaria cordata* (illustrated) is a common weed of cultivation in damp places all over the tropics. It has rounded, heart-shaped, hairless leaves and insignificant white flowers.

Polycarpaea. A genus of minute, much-branched erect herbs of dry sandy places. The small narrow leaves have large stipules between them, resembling the leaves. There are clusters of tiny flowers with five pointed petals. *Polycarpaea corymbosa* (illustrated) is a bushy herb a few inches high, of dry sandy places, and running through its whole life history in a few weeks.

Several other genera of this family occur in the tropics, but they are mostly confined to mountains.

AIZOIACEAE. This is a small family of fleshy plants sometimes called *Ficoidaceae*, adapted to live in dry or salty regions. Its most showy and interesting genus, *Mesembryanthemum*, is sub-tropical rather than tropical, and is confined to South Africa in the wild state, though often planted in gardens. The plants, Ice Plants and Hottentot Figs, have thick leaves closely packed together, and satiny flowers with numerous satiny 'petals' (really altered stamens) in various bright colours. One much less conspicuous member of the family, which occurs in many parts of the tropics, is **Sesuvium.** There are five species of this genus, all plants of salt marshes and other salty areas. In this genus the leaves, as usual, are opposite and fleshy, and the fleshy stem is procumbent. The flowers, which are solitary and axillary, have a superior ovary and five petal-like sepals with satiny sheen, which open in sunlight. The flowers are followed by capsules which open by a circular split. A pioneer on

26

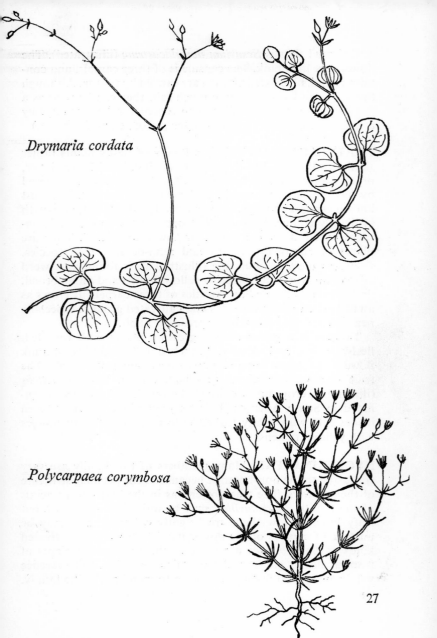

Drymaria cordata

Polycarpaea corymbosa

27

settled mud flats is *Sesuvium portulacastrum* (illustrated). The flowers are lilac-pink. The capsule is of three carpels, and contains round, black seeds, which are carried by the sea. Although the leaves and stems contain much salt, they can be used as a pot-herb, Sea Purslane. This plant is sometimes parasitized by a species of *Cuscuta* or Dodder (see p. 108, *Convolvulaceae*.)

PORTULACACEAE. This is a family of fleshy plants rather similar to the last, but it is at once distinguished by the hairy, or scaly, appendages to the stipules. The flowers are characterized by having only two sepals, and petals are present. The best known genus, **Portulaca,** has some pretty cultivated species with brilliantly coloured flowers that open in the sunshine, sometimes called 'Japanese Rose', or 'Jump and Kiss'. They are plants of sunny dry places and semi-deserts. One species, *Portulaca oleracea*, Purslane (illustrated), is found as a weed all over the world. It has satiny yellow flowers and rather broad, fleshy leaves, followed by capsules of three carpels. It grows as an annual on sandy waysides and cultivated ground, especially near the sea, and has a low, spreading habit.

Talinum is a genus of low growing plants with rounded, fleshy leaves, and slender, branched inflorescences of pink flowers, the petals being about twice as long as the sepals. The fruit is a capsule about two inches long. *Talinum patens* (illustrated) crops up on cultivated ground, and probably originated in South America. It is an erect plant about eighteen inches tall, with pretty forked inflorescences of pink flowers with yellow stamens.

NYCTAGINACEAE. Many members of this family are very confusing to the non-botanist because of the peculiar structure of their flowers. The true flowers, as in the best known genus of the family, *Bougainvillea*, may be quite inconspicuous, but leafy bracts below them are brightly coloured, and may be mistaken for parts of the flower itself. The various cultivated kinds of *Bougainvillea* are some of the best known plants of tropical flower gardens. An examination of an inflorescence will show several features common to members of the family,

28

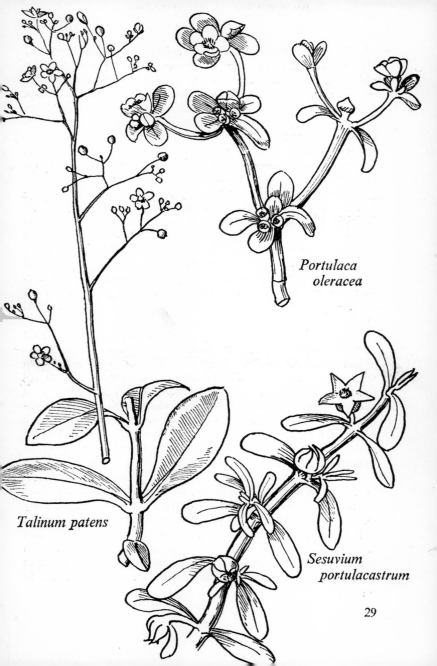

Portulaca oleracea

Talinum patens

Sesuvium portulacastrum

which contains trees, shrubs, and a few herbs. The flowers of *Bougainvillea* are in clusters of three, the central one being the oldest (a cymose arrangement). Each flower has a tubular perianth of only one whorl, enclosing five stamens and a superior ovary; the style is long and reaches the top of the tube. When the fruit develops it becomes dry and one-seeded (an achene). These flowers are greenish yellow or white, but surrounding them at the base are three broad, leafy bracts, brilliantly coloured and attractive to butterflies and other pollinators. The old perianth persists in the fruit and protects it.

The genus **Mirabilis,** Marvel of Peru, native to South America, has been naturalized in many tropical places. *Mirabilis jalapa* (illustrated) yields jalap, a purgative root. The plant is easily recognized by its brilliant crimson flowers with long tubular perianths, spreading into a five-lobed flower from which project five stamens and a stigma, coiled at first at the tip. At the base of the flower, united bracts form a false calyx. The inflorescence is cymose. The leaves, as in other members of the family, are opposite and stalked. Besides the crimson form occurs another with butter-coloured flowers. The fruit is black and ribbed. This plant is commonly found as an erect herb on rubbish heaps and waste land.

Boerhaavia, Hog Weed, is a genus of spreading, weedy herbs with opposite leaves of very unequal size, and cymose inflorescences of tiny crimson flowers. The fruit is covered with sticky glandular hairs which make it cling to passers-by. *Boerhaavia viscosa* (illustrated), a common weed of waste places, is a spreading plant a foot or more high, with leaves and stems covered with short sticky hairs. It is found in all tropical countries.

NYMPHAEACEAE. The Water Lily family. All its members are aquatic herbs with rhizomes rooting in shallow water. They generally have large, showy flowers, and large, simple leaves, either floating or aerial, but *Cabomba* has submerged divided leaves as well as small round floating ones. There are eight genera, most of which are familiar as ornamental plants in garden ponds. The most striking genus is **Victoria,** confined to

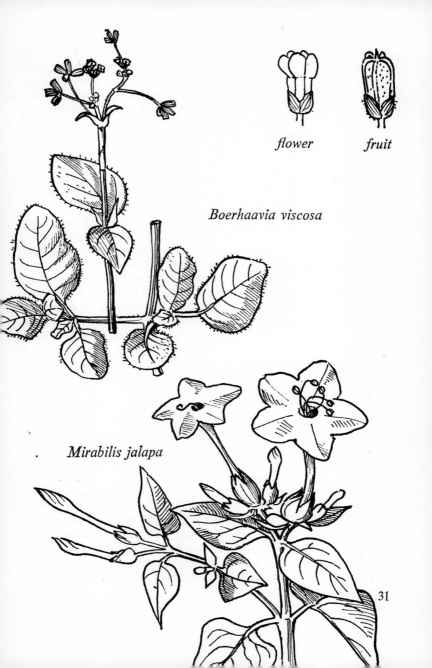

flower   fruit

Boerhaavia viscosa

Mirabilis jalapa

31

South America; one species, *V. amazonica*, has floating leaves shaped like enormous round trays six feet across, with raised rims and prickles beneath. The huge white flowers open in the evening and turn pink before fading the following day.

Cabomba. This is a genus with small star-shaped flowers, native to tropical America, where it blocks up waterways. The carpels are free. *Cabomba aquatica* (illustrated in colour, p. 33, Fig. 1) has yellow flowers with flower parts in threes. Its submerged stems are several feet in length and bear much divided leaves; the flowers are borne above the water supported by small simple floating leaves on the upper part of the stem. It makes a good aerating plant for the aquarium.

Nelumbium. In this genus the large plate-shaped leaves and showy, solitary flowers are held above the water on hairy stems several feet tall. These stems contain a milky latex. There are two species. *Nelumbium speciosum*, Sacred Lotus (illustrated in colour, p. 33, Fig. 2), has pink perianth leaves arranged spirally, the outer ones being smaller and greenish, and numerous yellow stamens. The free carpels are sunk in a peculiar raised torus which afterwards carries the fruits; these are edible, and known as Water Nuts. This plant is native to Eastern Asia, but has been introduced to many parts of the tropics, where it now grows in drainage trenches. The other species, native to America, is *N. luteum*. Its general form is similar but the flowers are clear yellow.

Nymphaea. This is the best known genus of Water Lilies, and various species occur throughout the tropics. It has rounded floating leaves and flowers raised above the water on much shorter stalks than those of *Nelumbium*. The flowers have four green sepals and numerous oblong petals, which in most species are white, but may be blue, pink, or yellow. *N. ampla* (illustrated in colour, p. 33, Fig. 3) is West Indian.

PAPAVERACEAE. The Poppy family is not well represented in the hot tropical regions, though it is an important family economically. From the Opium Poppy, *Papaver somniferum*, are obtained opium and morphine. Some members of the family are pernicious weeds in the temperate regions. All are herbs

1

2

3

33

with coloured juice. The leaves are alternate, without stipules, and often much divided. The flowers are often showy, but die quickly. They are regular, with four or more petals, numerous stamens and carpels, but only two sepals, which fall off when the flower opens. The carpels are united, the fruit being a capsule opening by valves or pores at the top, and the minute seeds are shaken out by the wind. There are twenty-eight genera, but only one, *Argemone*, is universal in the tropics.

Argemone. This is a genus of tropical American poppies. One species, *A. mexicana* (illustrated in colour, p. 34, Fig. 2), is now found in waste places all over the tropics. As long ago as the eighteenth century it had been noticed in Polynesia, where it must have been brought from America. It is a herb with prickly indented leaves and yellow flowers with four or six petals, numerous stamens and four to six carpels forming an ovary with sessile stigmas, often with a cross-like pattern. The fruit is a capsule opening by valves at the top, and bearing prickly hairs.

VIOLACEAE. In the temperate regions this family is best known for the Sweet Violet and other members of the genus **Viola,** but this genus does not occur in the tropics. The tropical genera are mostly trees and shrubs. The leaves are alternate, with stipules, and the flowers are solitary and axillary, with five petals, sepals and stamens, and three carpels. The members of the family are easily recognized by their flowers being irregular, with petals and sepals free, one petal often bearing a spur. The stamens are very short, and so placed that outgrowths from them form a box to catch the pollen. The fruit is explosive, with three valves. The genus **Hybanthus,** or **Ionidium,** is the best known of the tropical herbaceous genera. *Ionidium ipecacuanha* (illustrated in colour, p. 34, Fig. 1) yields the drug ipecacuanha. It is a herb with creeping underground parts and hairy stems and leaves.

CAPPARIDACEAE. The Caper family. This is a small tropical family, with about forty genera but a large number of species. Some are trees and woody climbers, including species of

Capparis (Caper), others are herbs. In most parts of the tropics this family takes the place of another family familiar in the temperate regions but rare in the tropics, *Cruciferae* (the Cabbage and Mustard family) and in both families a special kind of capsule, the *siliqua*, which is made of two carpels and has a false partition down the middle, occurs. The chief genera of herbs, which are spread throughout the tropics, are *Cleome* and *Gynandropsis*. The flowers are showy, with clawed petals.

Cleome. Herbs, often with glandular hairs, usually erect annuals with terminal racemes or corymbs of flowers and alternate, often compound leaves without stipules. There are many closely related species, all with white or mauve flowers, four petals alternating with four small sepals, and with either four or numerous long stamens. The torus is short. *Cleome triphylla* (illustrated) is an annual weed of damp, shady waste ground. It has white flowers. Some other species have spines.

Gynandropsis. A genus resembling the last except that the ovary is carried out on a stalk-like torus which also carries the filaments of the stamens, and there are usually six stamens. *Gynandropsis pentaphylla*, Bastard Mustard (illustrated), is a herb with unpleasantly scented glandular hairs, which grows on waste ground in many parts of the tropics. The seeds can be used in the same ways as those of true Mustard (*Brassica nigra*). Both genera have fruit of the siliqua form, with a false partition (replum) down the centre to which the seeds are attached. When the siliqua splits open, it does so from below upwards, leaving the seeds hanging for a time on the central partition.

Capers, used in flavouring sauces, etc., are the pickled flower buds of *Capparis spinosa*, which is a woody climber with attractive flowers and simple leaves, in the axils of which are large spines. It is cultivated in many parts of the tropics.

CRASSULACEAE. This is a very interesting family of succulent plants mostly found in dry parts of the tropics and in the sub-tropics, but they are rare in South America and in Australasia. Their chief centre of distribution is South Africa. Many are cultivated in gardens, but they are of no economic use. The members of the family are perennial herbs with fleshy leaves

36

Cleome triphylla

Gynandropsis pentaphylla

37

and stems, and tufted habit. They have amazing powers of vegetative reproduction, some producing little bulbils in the leaf axils, others regenerating from fallen leaves which make buds on their margins. The flowers are in cymose inflorescences, often small, but showy because of their large number and bright colour. They are very regular in construction, the flower parts usually being in fours or fives, or multiples of them. There are twenty-five genera, mostly found in sunny, rocky places, often high up on mountains. The two genera mentioned below are frequent on waste places, probably as garden escapes.

Kalanchoe. A genus of erect, branched, fleshy plants with red, orange or yellow flowers with their petals united to form a tube; there are four petals and eight stamens. The leaves are opposite. The calyx is much shorter than the corolla. *Kalanchoe crenata* (illustrated) has yellow or orange flowers and broad leaves with crenate (scalloped) margins.

Bryophyllum. A rather similar genus to the last, but the flowers are less numerous, and drooping; they have large inflated calyces. *Bryophyllum pinnatum*, Leaf of Life (illustrated), has green inflated calyces tinged with purple. It is an erect plant growing about two feet tall, with broad crenate leaves which fall in the dry season, giving rise to buds on the margin which grow into new plants. Various species of *Bryophyllum* are found throughout the tropics, especially in dry stony places, but their country of origin is uncertain.

The fruit of all members of *Crassulaceae* is similar. It is a group of follicles, containing numerous fine seeds which are dispersed by the wind.

SAXIFRAGACEAE. This family is hardly represented in the tropics at all, except on mountains in a few places. It is mentioned here on account of one small herbaceous plant which is quite common on dried-up ponds, damp fields, edges of ricefields and similar places, of the genus **Vahlia**. There are four species, all small, much-branched herbs less than a foot high, with opposite leaves and tiny white flowers, each with five petals, five sepals, five stamens and two united carpels forming

Kalanchoe crenata

flower

fruit

Bryophyllum pinnatum

39

an inferior ovary. *Vahlia oldenlandioides* (illustrated) looks extremely like *Oldenlandia*, a little herb of the Coffee family, which inhabits very similar situations. It is easily distinguished from *Oldenlandia* by its free, not united, petals.

The rest of this family consists of herbs with a low tufted habit, known as saxifrages, which mostly live on stony mountainsides in the temperate regions.

DROSERACEAE. This is a fascinating family of insect-eating herbs of very small size, with a rosette habit, which grow in acid, boggy places. In the tropics they are commonest, given suitable conditions, on high ground. The best known genus is **Drosera,** Sundew, of which there are altogether about ninety species, all of somewhat similar form, with spathulate leaves borne in a rosette on a reduced stem. These leaves are of very peculiar form, bearing long sticky glandular hairs which secrete a sweet fluid to attract small insects. The hairs are red, and their colour and dew-like sticky drops at their tips cause flies to settle on them. The flies are then stuck and trapped. The hairs bend over and the leaf slowly closes on the insect, which is then digested by enzymes secreted on the leaf surface. From the centre of the rosette (really on an axillary branch) arises a slender erect raceme of small white or pinkish flowers with parts in fives. The fruit is a capsule opening by slits at the sides, and the small seeds are blown away by the wind. *Drosera communis* (illustrated) is a South American species. Other species of Sundew are found all over the world on boggy places and on acid sand, often with Bog Moss (*Sphagnum*).

CONNARACEAE. This very small tropical family of climbing shrubs and trees makes an interesting link with the next family. It contains a number of plants with simple flowers with all their parts free, all the parts being in fives, except for the carpels, of which there is often only one. The flowers are regular, and the fruit is a simple kind of capsule called a follicle, made of a single carpel which opens all down one side when it is ripe. In this family the leaves are usually pinnately compound, and they are arranged alternately. They have no stipules.

40

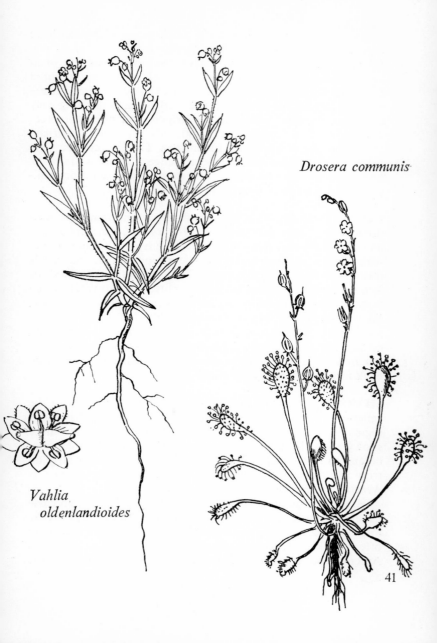

Drosera communis

*Vahlia
oldenlandioides*

41

Rourea. This and the closely allied genus **Connarus** have representatives in tropical Asia, Africa and America. All are much alike. They are wiry, woody twiners growing in open bushy places, with panicles of yellowish or cream coloured flowers with parts in fives, except for the single carpel. (There are two sets of five stamens.) The seed pods, containing only one seed, become swollen as they ripen, and often turn red. *Rourea revoluta*, Supple Jack (illustrated), is a South American species frequent on bushy savannahs. The flowers are pale yellow, and the ripe follicle bright orange. The seeds are black and are violently poisonous. The stems are twining or semi-erect, and the leaves have three leaflets.

LEGUMINOSAE. This huge and important family is now divided into three smaller ones, *Mimosaceae, Caesalpiniaceae* and *Papilionaceae*. They all agree in having alternate leaves with stipules, the leaves generally being compound, and simple flowers in raceme inflorescences. The typical fruit is a pod, or *legume*, made of one carpel which splits into two valves when ripe, but there are many variants. As in the previous family, the petals are free. Many members of the family are of great agricultural importance, as their roots bear nodules containing certain bacteria, which enable them to absorb nitrogen from the air so that they can live on very poor soils, and when dug back into the ground they enrich it.

MIMOSACEAE. The members of this family agree with the general features mentioned above. In addition they have regular flowers, and often numerous stamens which are more showy than the petals. A number of valuable timber trees belong to this group, but very few herbs. They are nearly all tropical. Among the members of economic importance is **Acacia,** which yields gum and tannin.

Mimosa. A genus with sensitive compound leaves and close heads of minute pink or white flowers. The fruit usually breaks into one-seeded pieces (a lomentum). The stems and leaves are often prickly. *Mimosa pudica*, Sensitive plant, is native to America, but is now common in waste places nearly all over

Schrankia
leptocarpa

Mimosa
asperata

Rourea revoluta

43

the tropics, on savannahs, airfields and other open places. It is a spreading prickly herb with compound, twice-pinnate leaves, and heads of pink flowers. When the leaves are touched, the four main leaflets hang down, and their pinnules close together. *Mimosa asperata* (illustrated) is a larger, shrubby species, also with sensitive leaves, and well armed with prickles. It has densely hairy fruits. This species has spread all over the tropics, where it may form dense low bush along river banks.

Schrankia is a very similar to *Mimosa*, but the fruits are cylindrical pods instead of flat lomenta. There are seven species, all natives of the warm parts of America. The one illustrated, *Schrankia leptocarpa*, is a pink-flowered, spreading, prickly plant closely resembling *Mimosa pudica* except for its characteristic pods. It has also spread to Africa and the East Indies.

Neptunia is a genus like *Mimosa* but with heads of yellow flowers, the outer ones of each head being barren, and resembling yellow petals. The fruit is a flat legume. The leaves are sensitive. *Neptunia prostrata* is an aquatic plant with a hollow floating stem, covered with white woolly hairs (illustrated in colour, p. 67, Fig. 3). It is found in shallow water all over the tropics.

CAESALPINIACEAE. In this family the characteristics listed in *Leguminosae* are found. In addition the flowers are always irregular, and in bud the posterior petal (the one next to the main stem) is folded beneath the others. The family includes a number of timber trees, including Purple Heart, dye woods and drugs, as well as a number of ornamental garden plants, and the well-known Tamarind tree.

The best known genus is **Cassia,** of which there are about four hundred species, many of which are common all over the tropics. In this genus the flowers are showy, with their petals almost equal in size. Of the ten stamens only seven are fertile, and their anthers open by pores at the top. The leaves are compoundly once-pinnate. The fruit is a legume or lomentum, often with 'false' partitions across it. *Cassia occidentalis*, Negro Coffee (illustrated), is a common herb, often woody at the base, with smooth pointed leaflets and not very showy pale

44

Caesalpinia crista

Cassia occidentalis

45

yellow flowers, followed by pods which are long and slightly flattened. The seeds have sometimes been roasted and ground as a substitute for coffee. The plant occurs on waste ground, roadsides and fields all over the tropics. It is disliked by stock, and survives in very over-grazed areas

There are numerous other herbaceous species of *Cassia*, as well as a number of trees, mostly with yellow flowers. Another common species, especially near the sea, is *Cassia alata*, with large broad leaflets and showy terminal racemes of orange-yellow flowers, which have large yellow bracts beneath them. The pods have four winged ridges. In the West Indies this plant is called 'Carrion Crow Bush'.

In the genus **Caesalpinia** the leaves are twice pinnate, and the plant is often prickly. The posterior petal of the flower is altered to form a trumpet-shaped nectary. *Caesalpinia pulcherrima*, Barbados Pride, is a well-known garden shrub or small tree with orange red or yellow flowers. *Caesalpinia crista*, Grey Nicker Bean (illustrated), is a woody scrambling climber of beach scrub; it also occurs in some places inland. It has racemes of small yellow flowers, and short, swollen, very prickly pods, each containing two hard grey seeds resembling small pebbles, which are often dispersed by the sea.

The genus **Bauhinia** has racemes of showy flowers, often white or pink, the plants being easily recognized by their two-lobed leaves and flat pods. Most of them are trees, but some are woody climbers or lianas of the high forest, such as *Bauhinia kunthiana*, Monkey Ladder, a South American species (illustrated in colour, p. 67, Fig. 2).

The most important, economically, of the three leguminous families is **PAPILIONACEAE**. In various parts of the world members of the family provide a very large amount of food for humans and stock, in the form of peas, beans, ground nuts, clover, alfalfa, soya, and many others. It is this family in which root nodules containing nitrogen-fixing bacteria are well developed, and most crop rotations require a leguminous crop of this kind. Members of the family are easily recognized by the form of the flower, which has one large petal at the back (the

Sesbania aegyptiaca

Tephrosia hookeriana

Indigofera suffruticosa

47

standard), two *wing* petals at the sides, and two, often partially united, *keel* petals in front. This special irregular form has the standard petal folded over the others in bud. (Contrast with *Caesalpiniaceae*.) There are very many herbaceous genera both in the tropical and temperate regions, many being climbers; there are also many trees. In most cases all stamens, or all but one, are united by their filaments to form a sheath round the ovary. The characteristic legume fruit may be modified in various ways. The following three herbaceous genera have legumes, and their leaves are pinnately compound. All the anthers are alike.

Tephrosia. Crimson, purple, white, or pale yellow flowering plants with terminal racemes. Their leaves are pinnately compound. Most are perennials which shoot again from the root when cut or burnt. Some are used as fish poisons. There are numerous species, mostly growing on savannahs and open bush. *Tephrosia hookeriana* (illustrated) has tall erect racemes of crimson, purple and white flowers. It is an under shrub with whitish hairs on the leaves.

Sesbania, Swamp Pea. A genus of quick growing annuals or short-lived woody plants. *S. grandiflora*, a small tree with deep pink and white flowers of large size, is widely cultivated in the tropics, the flowers being edible. The flowers in this genus are in axillary racemes, and the fruit is long and slender. *Sesbania aegyptiaca* (illustrated) is a herb about ten feet tall, which grows on damp waste places, especially near the sea. The yellow flowers are dotted with grey on the back as a rule.

Indigofera, Indigo. There are many species of this genus, mostly with salmon-red or pink flowers in axillary racemes, followed by small, sometimes curved, pods. The stamen next to the standard petal is free from the others. *Indigofera tinctoria*, which yields the dye indigo, has been widely cultivated all over the tropics. *Indigofera suffruticosa* (illustrated) is a rank-smelling low shrub with greyish green leaves and salmon-red flowers which grows on waste places near the sea. It is also cultivated. The fruits are bent into a semicircle.

Crotalaria, Shak-shak. A genus of showy herbs and under shrubs with terminal racemes differing from the three mentioned

48

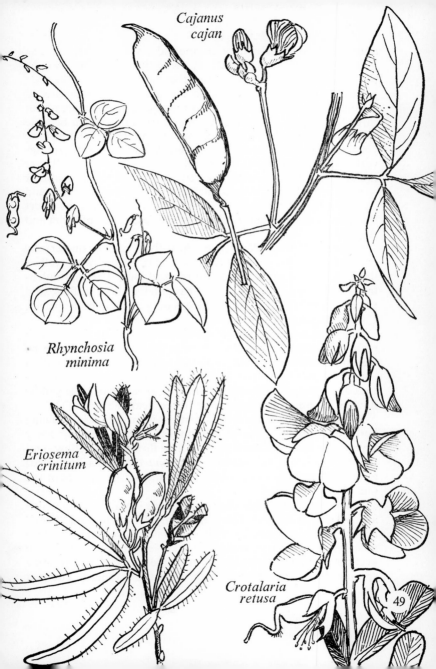

Cajanus cajan

Rhynchosia minima

Eriosema crinitum

Crotalaria retusa

49

above in having palmately compound or simple leaves. The flowers are nearly always yellow, the anthers are of two kinds, but the stamens are all joined together at the base, and the style is sharply bent near the base. The fruits are many-seeded legumes which become inflated as they mature. There are about three hundred and fifty species, mostly annuals which become woody at the base, with erect habit and terminal racemes. *Crotalaria retusa* (illustrated), a showy large-flowered species with rather broad leaves and small stipules, is common all over the tropics. It is sometimes cultivated for its fibre. Another species, with larger, scented flowers, more slender stems and narrower leaves, *Crotalaria juncea*, Sunn Hemp, Madras Sweet Pea, is a more frequently cultivated species, native of India and Australia.

Cajanus, Pigeon Pea, is a short-lived shrub universally cultivated in the tropics for its edible seeds, with yellow flowers and flat pods which are marked with diagonal indentations between the seeds. The leaves have three leaflets, and are covered with silky hairs. There is only one common species, *Cajanus cajan* (illustrated).

Rhynchosia is a genus of trailing or climbing beans with trifoliate leaves gland-dotted beneath, a feature which can be seen if the leaves are held up to the light and examined with a lens. The pods have only two seeds. *Rhynchosia minima* (illustrated) is a slender climbing plant with racemes of little yellow flowers, common amongst grass, often near the sea.

Eriosema. Members of this genus are mostly low-growing herbs and undershrubs of savannahs, often with very hairy leaves, usually with three leaflets. The flowers are yellow, and the flat pods are two-seeded. *Eriosema crinitum* (illustrated) grows in South America. Many other species are natives of the Old World tropics.

Phaseolus. This genus of twining beans includes many which are of use as human food, including 'Runner' and 'Lima' beans. They are plants with trifoliate leaves and axillary racemes of flowers in which the style is spirally twisted. The keel petals may be united to form a tube round it, and in some species the wing petals are larger than the standard. The pod

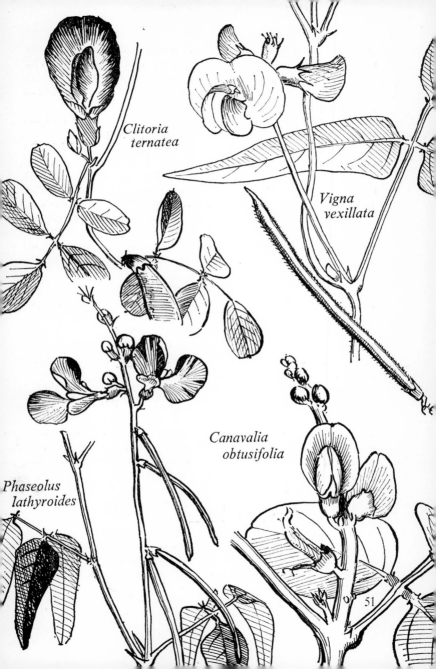

*Clitoria
ternatea*

*Vigna
vexillata*

*Canavalia
obtusifolia*

*Phaseolus
lathyroides*

51

is slightly flattened and contains a number of seeds. Many species grow in open scrubby places and savannahs. The species illustrated, *Phaseolus lathyroides*, has maroon flowers and the stems are only slightly twining. It has been introduced to various tropical places, possibly as a forage plant.

In the genus **Clitoria** the keel is not twisted spirally, and the stamen opposite the standard is free to the base. The standard is much larger than the other petals, and the style bears hairs on one side. *Clitoria ternatea*, Blue Vine (illustrated), has brilliant blue flowers. It is sometimes cultivated, but is also found wild in bushy places in most parts of the tropics. Many other species, with blue, pink, mauve, or white flowers occur.

Centrosema is a very similar genus common in tropical America. The showy flowers have the keel petals joined together, and the flowers are clustered at the top of the stem, with large bracts below them. The pods have lateral wings, making them four-sided.

Canavalia, Sword Bean. Some members of this genus are edible. The plants are rampant growing twiners with stout racemes of white or purple flowers, followed by thick pods containing large beans. The pods have well-marked ridges along the upper margin. *Canavalia obtusifolia*, Purple Seaside Bean (illustrated), is a common trailing plant of sandy tropical shores.

Vigna. This genus includes several edible beans, notably the well-known Black-eye. The flowers are clustered at the top of the raceme. The standard petal is very wide, and much larger than the other petals. The stigma is one-sided, and the style hairy near the top. The flowers are mauve or yellow. *V. vexillata*, Wayside Bean (illustrated), is a common mauve-flowered twiner in open bushy places. The scented flowers open mauve and quickly fade to buff. The pods are narrow and cylindrical. There are many other species.

Dolichos, Lablab, is a cultivated bean rather like Vigna but with wide flat pods. The stigma is not one-sided.

Mucuna. Cowitch, Horse Eye and Velvet Beans are members of this genus of tall twining plants. The racemes have the flowers in terminal heads which hang down, and the large fat

52

*Mucuna
sloanei*

*Zornia
diphylla*

*Abrus
precatorius*

*Calopogonium
mucunoides*

53

pods are covered with stinging hairs. *M. sloanei* (illustrated) has yellow flowers and deeply ridged pods. It is a native of the American tropics.

Calopogonium is another American genus of twining beans. The small blue flowers are in whorl-like clusters on the inflorescence stem. *Calopogonium mucunoides* (illustrated) is a common weed on barren sandy ground. It could probably be used as a green cover crop in the same way as Velvet Bean (*Mucuna*).

Many leguminous trees have bright red, or red and black seeds, used as beads and other ornaments. There is a climbing pea genus with shining red and black seeds, the genus **Abrus**. *A. precatorius*, Crabs' Eyes or Buck Beads (illustrated), is a common climbing plant in bushy places on sandy ground all over the tropics. The leaves are pinnately compound, and the flowers are reddish mauve, followed by pods which open to expose scarlet and black seeds. The seeds are violently poisonous.

In the last five genera to be mentioned in this very large family, the fruit, instead of being a pod, is a lomentum, which in most cases breaks up into one-seeded pieces. They are none of them climbing plants.

Zornia is a genus of slender erect plants in which the lomentum is covered with bristles. The leaves, which have two or four slender leaflets, have stipules with appendages at their bases. *Zornia diphylla* (illustrated) is found on very poor soil as a weed in many parts of the tropics. It has yellow flowers.

Arachis is rather peculiar in having fruits which develop under the earth. *Arachis hypogaea*, Pea-nut, Ground-nut (illustrated), is native to sandy places in South America, but is now planted all over the tropics and runs wild in many places. It has leaves with four wide leaflets, and solitary yellow flowers, only some of which are fertile. The 'nuts' are the oily seeds, which develop in fibrous lomenta underground.

Aeschynomene is an interesting genus in which the flowers are pea-shaped, but the leaves are sensitive like those of *Mimosa*. They are once-pinnate. The lomenta are very flat, and covered with minute hooked hairs to catch passers-by and

54

Aeschynomene sensitiva

Alysicarpus vaginalis

Desmodium incanum

Stylosanthes viscosa

Arachis hypogaea

55

disperse the seeds. *A. sensitiva* (illustrated) is found in damp places all over the tropics. It has yellow flowers. The stems have rather sticky hairs, and grow to about four feet.

Desmodium has fruits like *Aeschynomene* but the leaf is trifoliate or unifoliate and the flowers reddish or blue. Various species, usually perennial, are weeds amongst grass. *Desmodium incanum*, Sweethearts (illustrated), is an erect species, rather woody at the base, growing about two feet tall. The flowers are crimson or bluish. It is common in both hemispheres.

Stylosanthes is like a small-leaved, yellow-flowered *Desmodium* with the calyx tube slender and stalk-like. The stipules form a sheath at the base of the leaf. *Stylosanthes viscosa* (illustrated) is a small spreading species often found on sandy ground in many parts of the tropics. Its stems and leaves are covered with short, sticky hairs.

Alysicarpus. This genus includes several species which grow with *Desmodium* in grassy places, but they are easily distinguished by having short cylindrical, not flattened fruits, and the flowers are smaller, usually set closer together. *A. vaginalis*, Horse Weed (illustrated), and other species are common crimson-flowered herbs of grass land all over the tropics.

FAMILY OXALIDACEAE. This is a small family with only seven genera, to which two common tropical fruit trees belong: the Cucumber Tree or Bilimbi, with small acid fruits, and the Coolie Tamarind or Five Fingers, with yellow, acid, five-sided fruit. Both belong to the genus **Averrhoa**. The other well-known genus, **Oxalis**, consists of small herbs with acid juice in their leaves and stems, and leaves with three leaflets, the simple, regular flowers being pink, white, or yellow. The fruit is a capsule of five carpels, from which seeds shoot out by an explosive mechanism when touched. *Oxalis corniculata* (illustrated) is a yellow-flowered herb with most of the flowers in pairs. The trifoliate leaves are often dark red. It is a common weed of cultivated ground in most tropical countries.

Biophytum. This genus resembles *Oxalis* except that the leaves are pinnately compound. *Biophytum apodiscias* (illustrated) is a small herb with a rosette of leaves sensitive to touch. It has

*Biophytum
apodiscias*

Oxalis corniculata

*Tribulus
cistoides*

*Quassia
amara*

57

orange-red flowers in small heads. It is common as a weed on waste ground in the Old World tropics.

FAMILY ZYGOPHYLLACEAE. This small tropical family contains trees, shrubs and herbs which flourish in dry places. To this family belongs the Lignum Vitae tree (**Guaiacum**). The commonest genus of herbs is **Tribulus**. The leaves are pinnately compound, and opposite, one leaf of each pair being much smaller than the other. The leaves bear stipules at the base, and the plant looks superficially like a member of *Leguminosae*. The flowers are showy and regular, with their parts in fours or fives. The fruit is characteristically four or five-sided and armed with spines. It breaks into pieces each containing several seeds. *Tribulus cistoides* (illustrated) is a spreading herb of waste ground, with bright yellow, showy flowers, commonly called Caltrops, or Savannah Buttercup.

FAMILY SIMARUBACEAE. This is a family of trees and woody plants usually with pinnately compound leaves, characteristically having the stalk and rachis winged. Many have a bitter principle in the bark. Quassia, used as an insecticide, is obtained from *Quassia amara* (illustrated), usually a low-growing shrub found in sandy places near rivers. It has brilliant crimson-scarlet flowers with projecting stamens for pollination by birds, followed by nut-like fruits in clusters of five on a coloured receptacle. It is a native of tropical America.

FAMILY POLYGALACEAE. In this family the flowers have a superficial resemblance to those of the pea family. They are generally brightly coloured. The ovary has more than one carpel, and the fruit is never a legume. Two genera are widely distributed in the tropics.

Securidaca. This genus consists of woody plants, often climbers, with compound leaves and white or puce-coloured pea-like flowers. These are followed by winged fruits each containing one seed. *Securidaca paniculata* (illustrated) is rather peculiar in having simple leaves. It is a native of tropical America, a high climber with puce flowers in showy clusters.

58

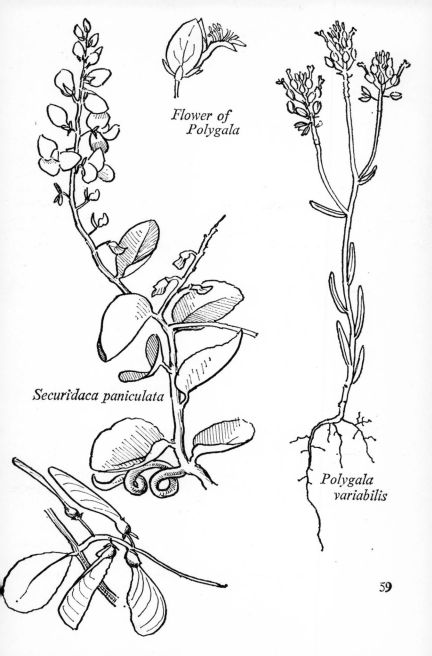

Flower of
Polygala

Securidaca paniculata

Polygala
variabilis

59

Polygala, Milkwort, is a genus which occurs all over the world. All the members are herbs, usually of grassy places. Many are annuals which spring up in the rainy season and shed their seeds at the beginning of the dry season. The species illustrated is *P. variabilis*, which has crimson-purple flowers and simple narrow leaves. The fruit is a capsule.

FAMILY EUPHORBIACEAE. This is a large family, and very important economically, though most of its members have very insignificant flowers. Many are trees, others are shrubs, herbs, and climbers. A number of them contain a milky latex, which is often poisonous, as in the famous Manchineel Tree, **Hippomane,** of the West Indies. The latex of *Hevea brasiliensis* is the chief source of natural rubber. Some members of the family have swollen edible roots, as in *Manihot*, Cassava, a native of Tropical America, which is now extensively cultivated all over the tropics. A few members of the family have fleshy drupes, such as the very poisonous Manchineel mentioned above, and the edible Otaheite Gooseberry, *Phyllanthus acidus*, a native of south east Asia, but most of the family are easily distinguished by their characteristic explosive fruit, usually with three carpels, which breaks up suddenly and releases three seeds at the same moment, often to a distance of many yards. The flowers are always unisexual. The male flowers often have a perianth, but the female ones are naked. In the large genus *Euphorbia* there is a special arrangement of flowers, a central stalked female one being surrounded by male flowers so reduced as to resemble stamens. The whole cluster is surrounded by a sheath bearing four crescent-shaped glands, and on casual inspection looks like a single flower. In *Euphorbia pulcherrima*, Poinsettia, inflorescences like this are surrounded by brilliant red leaves. Some desert-loving species resemble Cacti, having thick spiny stems and no leaves, but the milky latex distinguishes them.

Phyllanthus. In this genus the simple leaves are regularly arranged on short stems so that they imitate compound leaves, and the separate male and female flowers in the leaf axils appear to be growing on the compound leaf. There

60

Jatropha
gossypiifolia

Phyllanthus niruri

Caperonia
castaneifolia

Croton flavens

61

are numerous species, some woody, and some herbs. *Phyllanthus niruri* (illustrated) is a common annual weed on cultivated ground.

Jatropha. In this genus of small fleshy shrubs male flowers have five petals and eight stamens. The flowers are in spreading cymes. The leaves bear gland hairs, which in *J. urens* sting like a nettle. The leaves are palmately lobed. *Jatropha gossypiifolia*, Belly-ache Bush (illustrated), is a species with maroon-coloured flowers and shiny leaves. It is common in many parts of the tropics, and is sometimes planted near villages. It flourishes near the sea, and on over-grazed land, where it remains untouched by stock. The explosive fruits resemble those of Castor Oil.

Croton. This is a genus of shrubs or herbs woody at the base, which have simple leaves often densely hairy beneath. The spike-like inflorescence is terminal, the male flowers having numerous stamens. The various species mostly inhabit poor soil, often on rocky places. *Croton flavens* (illustrated) is a common grey-leaved low-growing shrub on the cliffs in Barbados. The so-called 'Crotons' of gardens belong to a different genus, *Codiaeum*.

Caperonia is a genus of slender hairy herbs with flowers like *Croton* except that the stamens are joined to form a tube. The fruit is prickly. *Caperonia castaneifolia* (illustrated) is a weed of damp ground, with bristly narrow leaves.

Manihot. There are various similar species and hybrids of this genus, all native to tropical America. *M. esculenta*, and a few other species, produce fleshy roots (Cassava or Mandioc) from which starch, farine, and tapioca are prepared. The raw root of both 'sweet' and 'bitter' cassava is poisonous, but the poison is dispersed by grating, washing and heating. Cultivated Cassava often fails to produce flowers. The leaves are palmately divided.

Ricinus. There is only one species of this genus, *R. communis* (illustrated), the Castor Oil plant. It is a native of Africa, but has been introduced to all tropical countries. The oil is obtained from the seeds, which are contained in a prickly explosive fruit of the typical *Euphorbia* type. The stamens of the male

phorbia
ypericifolia

Tragia volubilis

Ricinus
communis

Dalechampia
scandens

63

flowers are branched. *Ricinus* is a very tall herb with large, palmately lobed leaves. It grows wild on waste ground.

Tragia. A genus of erect or twining herbs with stinging hairs. The flowers are in axillary spikes or racemes with the male ones at the top. The male flowers have only three stamens. *Tragia volubilis*, Nettle Vine (illustrated), has simple leaves, and twines in bushy places in many parts of the tropics.

Dalechampia. Another genus of twining climbers, distinguished from the last by having the flowers clustered together at the end of an axillary stalk, and surrounded by two wide, sheathing bracts. In one species the bracts are white. *Dalechampia scandens* (illustrated) has pale green bracts and deep three-lobed leaves. It occurs in bushy places in tropical America, Africa and Arabia.

Euphorbia. This is the biggest genus of the family, all its members having the peculiar flower structure already described, and all containing copious milky latex. *Euphorbia hypericifolia* (illustrated) is a semi-prostrate, branched annual weed of waste ground, with smooth oblong leaves minutely indented on the margins. The flowers are in tiny cymes in the leaf axis. It is a common weed in all warm countries.

FAMILY SAPINDACEAE. This is a tropical family which consists almost entirely of trees or shrubs, but there are five genera of climbers. To this family belong the well-known tropical fruits Litchi and Akee. The members of the family have alternate, pinnately compound leaves, and cymes of small flowers, which are irregular and unisexual. The flower parts, except the carpels, are in fours or fives, and there are usually three carpels. The fruit is often red; it may be fleshy or a capsule, or a winged fruit. The climbers have peculiar tendrils, usually branched, and coiled like watch springs.

Paullinia. A genus of climbing plants with watch-spring tendrils from the leaf axils, and clusters of small greenish or white flowers. The leaves are pinnately compound with a terminal leaflet. The fruit is a crimson capsule with three seeds. *Paullinia pinnata* (illustrated) is a common bush climber in both tropical Africa and America.

64

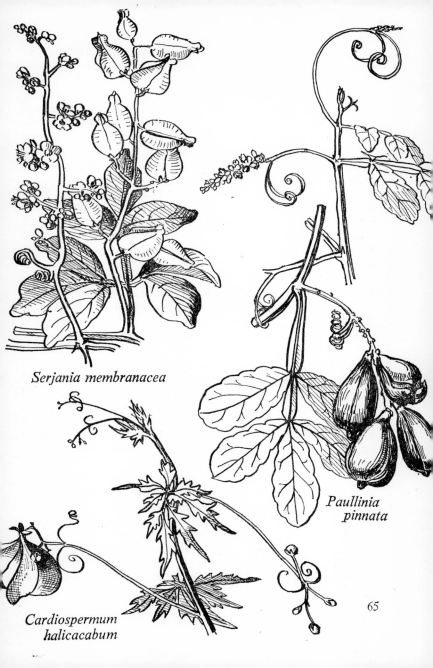

Serjania membranacea

Paullinia pinnata

Cardiospermum halicacabum

Serjania is a tropical American genus similar to the last, but producing three-sided winged fruits which break into one-seeded pieces. There are nearly two hundred species. *Serjania membranacea* (illustrated) is a scrambling climber of dry bushy places. The winged fruits are pale brown with a satiny sheen.

Cardiospermum, Heart Pea, Balloon Vine. The leaves in this genus have deeply cut leaflets. The small white flowers are followed by inflated, winged capsules. *Cardiospermum helicacabum* (illustrated) is a slender climber. The seeds in the capsule are dull blue.

Dodonea. A genus of shrubs and trees having small green flowers and simple leaves. The fruit is flat with two or three wings. *Dodonea viscosa* (illustrated) is a small sea coast shrub a few feet tall, with cymose clusters of small green flowers and flat winged fruits. The plant is slightly sticky. It is found on all tropical coasts.

FAMILY VITACEAE. The Grape family. Most of its members are tendril-climbers, the tendrils being opposite the leaves. The flowers are very small and simple, regular, with their flower parts in fours or fives. The fruit is a berry. The flowers are borne in large cymose clusters, and produce nectar which attracts flies. In the tropics the commonest genus is **Cissus**. In this genus the leaves are simple or palmately compound, and the fruits have four seeds. The tendrils never bear flowers, and are simple or branched. *Cissus quadrangularis* (illustrated) is an interesting species common in dry areas in the Old World and also introduced to tropical America. It has four-sided, winged stems, and leaves are present only on the young shoots. The berries are red and shiny.

BALSAMINACEAE. This is a very easily recognized family as there is only one important genus, **Impatiens**, Touch-me-not, or Balsam. The plants are succulent herbs with watery juice and simple alternate leaves. The flowers, borne in the leaf axils, are irregular with one sepal drawn out to a long spur. The fruit is an explosive capsule of five carpels which breaks up and sheds the seeds when touched. There are many species, some of which

66

68

are favourite garden and house plants. Many inhabit wet places at high altitudes on tropical mountains. *Impatiens sultani* (= *walleriana*), (illustrated in colour, p. 68, Fig. 3) commonly grown as a house plant or in shady gardens, is an Asiatic species.

FAMILY TILIACEAE. This family largely consists of trees, but there are a few herbaceous members, mostly woody at the base and with stamens containing fibres which are of commercial value. **Tilia** is the 'Lime' or Linden Tree of the temperate regions. **Corchorus** is the Jute plant. Plants of this family are recognized by their simple, regular flowers, arranged in cymes, with numerous stamens, which may be united in groups, but never into a tube round the style, as in the next two families. The leaves bear stipules, and often have branched hairs, a characteristic which is more easily seen under the microscope. In bud the sepals meet but do not overlap, a condition described as valvate.

Corchorus. In this genus the leaves often bear paired bristles-like tails at the base of the leaf blade. The fruit is a beaked capsule, which develops from a small yellow flower; the flowers are clustered in the leaf axils. Several species yield jute fibre. *Corchorus aestuans* (illustrated) and several similar species occur as weeds of cultivation in various parts of the tropics.

Grewia. In this genus, which includes some shrubs as well as herbs, the petals have glands at the base. The fruits are small and berry-like. *Grewia villosa* (illustrated) has broad leaves with slightly lobed edges. The flowers are yellow, and the fruit is covered with short hairs. It is found usually in rocky places, all over the Old World tropics. It is a shrubby plant, growing ten feet or more high.

FAMILY MALVACEAE. This is an easy family to recognize because of the peculiar flower structure. The flowers are usually large and showy, with five joined sepals and five petals; the stamens are very numerous, attached to the petals and joined to form a complete tube round the style. The stigmas project beyond this tube at the top. If the pollen is examined it is found to be prickly. A single pollen grain of this family is a beautiful object to observe under the microscope. The fruit often breaks up into one-seeded pieces, but in the well-known genus *Hibiscus*, in *Gossypium* (cotton) and some others it is a capsule. The plants contain much mucilage, and their stems often contain fibres of commercial value. Most of the family are herbs and shrubs, and many are tropical.

Wissadula. In this genus of spreading erect herbs, the flowers have a simple calyx without an 'epicalyx' of bracts surrounding it. The fruit, made of five carpels, spreads in a star-shaped pattern when ripe, and opens to let out the seeds. *Wissadula periplocifolia* (illustrated) is a slender plant with white flowers and elongated heart-shaped leaves, sometimes found on waste ground. There are other species with orange and yellow flowers.

Abutilon. In this genus the flowers are often solitary in the leaf axils, and the fruit has ten or more carpels, each with several seeds. The leaves are heart-shaped as in the previous genus, or slightly lobed, a characteristic which has given some species the name 'Flowering Maple'. They are shrubs or herbs. *Abutilon indicum* (illustrated) is a species with orange-yellow flowers and fruits with twenty or more carpels. The softly-downy leaves are pointed, with an indented margin. The ripe fruit is black. It is common in waste places, especially on alkaline soil, in most parts of the tropics.

Sida, Wire Weed or Twelve-o'clock Broom. A very confusing genus of small shrubs with slender wiry stems and usually pale orange-yellow flowers with a satiny sheen, which open early and fade by midday. The genus is distinguished, like the above two, by not having an epicalyx of bracts below the calyx, and differs from them in having a separating fruit in which each carpel has only one seed and does not open. *Sida carpinifolia* (illustrated) is a species with nearly hairless, lanceolate leaves with a serrated margin, short stalks and well developed stipules. The flowers are pale orange yellow, and produce fruits made of seven or eight carpels (the stigmas in this genus are double the number of carpels). The carpels each have two sharp beaks. This plant is a wiry herb or small shrub growing up to five feet or more. Fibres from its stem are sometimes used for making rope, and its fine wiry stems for making brooms. It is a common roadside weed in most parts of the tropics.

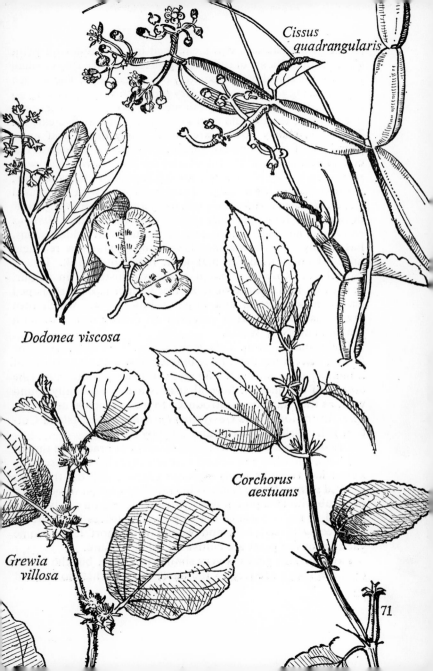

Cissus
quadrangularis

Dodonea viscosa

Corchorus
aestuans

Grewia
villosa

71

The genus **Hibiscus** was mentioned in the chapter on plant classification. Plants of this genus generally have a ring of small bracts – the epicalyx, immediately below the calyx. The stamen tube, bearing the stamens, is very long, the very tip having no stamens, but ending in five minute leaf-like points. There are five stigmas, the capsule fruit being composed of five carpels. The large, showy flowers are borne singly in the leaf axils. Members of the genus are shrubs, small trees, or herbs. The cultivated forms are known all over the tropics. *Hibiscus rosa-sinensis*, a woody plant with showy red, pink or yellow flowers, is often planted as a hedge. There are forms with variegated leaves. *Hibiscus esculentus*, a tall, hairy annual plant with yellow flowers and long, pod-like capsules, is the Ochra. *Hibiscus sabdariffa*, more slender than the last, often with reddish stems, has a calyx which becomes fleshy and contains a red acid juice which is used for making a refreshing drink. This is 'Sorrel', or Roselle. *Hibiscus tiliaceus* (illustrated in colour, p. 68, Fig. 1) is a shrub or small tree with broad, heart-shaped leaves, pale beneath, and bright yellow flowers which turn orange as they fade. It is common on muddy coasts of both the Old and New World.

Gossypium, Cotton. This genus differs from *Hibiscus* in the flower, since it has three large bracts below the calyx instead of a number of small ones. The seeds bear long white hairs (the cotton of commerce). Several species are occasionally found wild, as they have been introduced to many tropical countries. The illustration shows *Gossypium barbadense*, Sea Island Cotton. It has yellow flowers, and shrubby habit.

Urena. In this genus there is an epicalyx of bracts like that of *Hibiscus*, but they are joined to each other at the base. The flower has twice as many styles as carpels, and the fruit has hooked spines. *Urena lobata* (illustrated) is a tough woody herb or shrub with rose pink flowers, which is found on sandy waste ground in many parts of the tropics. The leaves are more or less deeply three-lobed, and woolly with short hairs. Some varieties of the plant are cultivated for their fibre.

Pavonia. This genus is very similar to *Urena*, but the bracts of the epicalyx are free to the base; the fruit has no hooked

Sida
carpinifolia

Abutilon
indicum

Wissadula
periplocifolia

Gossypium
barbadense

73

spines, but often has barbed bristles. There are many species, with pink, white, or yellow flowers, none of which appears to be common to both Old and New World. *Pavonia cancellata* (illustrated) is a prostrate plant of sandy savannah regions in South America. It is very hairy in all parts, and has showy yellow flowers with a purple blotch at the base of each petal. The points on the carpel walls of the separating fruit catch on clothes so that they get dispersed.

Malachra is a genus resembling *Hibiscus* except that the styles are double the number of carpels, and the flowers are in clusters surrounded by leafy bracts. *Malachra capitata* (illustrated) is a tough, erect perennial herb with bristly hairs and rounded leaves. The flowers are yellow or white. It is a native of the West Indies, but has spread to many parts of the tropics.

Cienfuegosia. Another genus like *Hibiscus* but with almost undivided styles. The seeds have cottony hairs. *Cienfuegosia affinis* (illustrated) is an erect herb with yellow flowers, the petals having a purple blotch at the base. It is South American.

Malvastrum. This genus closely resembles *Sida* in general appearance, and is common in similar places, but the flower has an epicalyx. The fruit of *Malvastrum tricuspidatum*, one of the commonest species, has three sharp spines. The flowers are yellow, and remain open longer than those of *Sida*.

FAMILY STERCULIACEAE. To this group belong the Cacao Tree (**Theobroma**) and the **Cola** Nut. Most of the family are woody plants. They are distinguished by having two sets of stamens, the inner ones united as a rule to form a tube. There is usually only one style and stigma, and the flowers may be unisexual; in some genera there are no petals. They are regular, with superior ovaries.

Helicteres. This is an interesting genus of small shrubs found in most parts of the tropics except Africa. The flowers have a long tubular calyx and five petals. Ten stamens are joined to form a tube surrounding an outgrowth which carries out the ovary on a stalk. As the fruit develops, the separate carpels twist round each other spirally. *Helicteres isora* (illustrated) is a savannah shrub with scarlet flowers. The leaves are whitish with fine hairs.

74

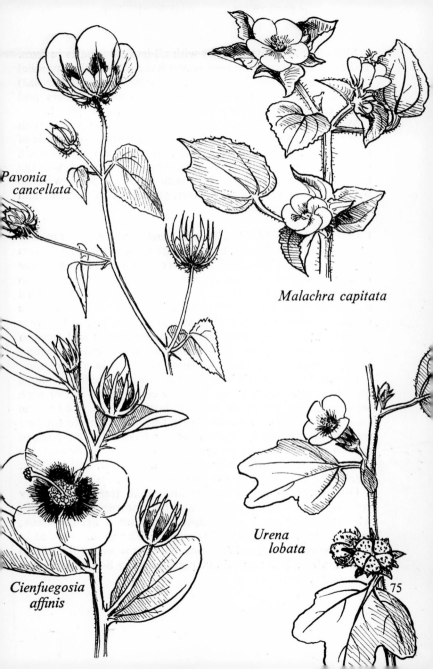

*Pavonia
cancellata*

Malachra capitata

*Cienfuegosia
affinis*

*Urena
lobata*

75

Melochia. A genus of herbs with all its flower parts in fives. The simple, pinnately veined leaves have well-marked parallel lateral veins and slender stipules. *Melochia hirsuta* (illustrated) is an erect savannah plant with crimson-purple flowers and leaves covered with silky hairs. The genus is widespread.

Waltheria is a tropical genus of low shrubby plants with hairy leaves, in which the fruit is a one-seeded capsule made of two carpels. *Waltheria americana*, Velvet Bush (illustrated), originating in tropical America, has spread to most parts of the tropics, generally on dry soils or semi-deserts. It is a low shrub with its leaves covered with short, grey, silky hairs. The small flowers are golden yellow.

FAMILY OCHNACEAE. This tropical family consists mainly of shrubs and small trees, but there are a few herbs. The flowers are regular, and arranged in cymes or racemes. The flower parts are in fives, and the carpels are generally free below so that a collection of simple fruits develops, often on an enlarged coloured receptacle as in *Ochna*. The alternate leaves are pinnately veined, the lateral veins being parallel. The family is divided into two sections, the first being shrubs and trees in which the fruit is a nut or drupe (stone fruit) and the second herbs producing capsules with three valves as in *Sauvagesia*.

Ochna. This is an Old World genus in which the flowers have numerous stamens. The flowers have conspicuous red or pink sepals, and the receptacle becomes large and red, holding the small fleshy fruits. This and the next genus belong to the first section of the family. *Ochna mossambicensis* is an African species often grown as an ornamental plant. The flowers are yellow, the sepals and receptacle are bright red, and the fruit black. The petals fall by the early afternoon.

Ouratea. A genus of shrubs and small trees with showy yellow flowers like the last, but with ten stamens, the anthers of which open by pores at the apex. The fruit is usually black, mounted on an enlarged red receptacle. The genus is found in both tropical Africa and America. *Ouratea superba* (illustrated) is a shrub or low tree of wet places on the South American savannahs.

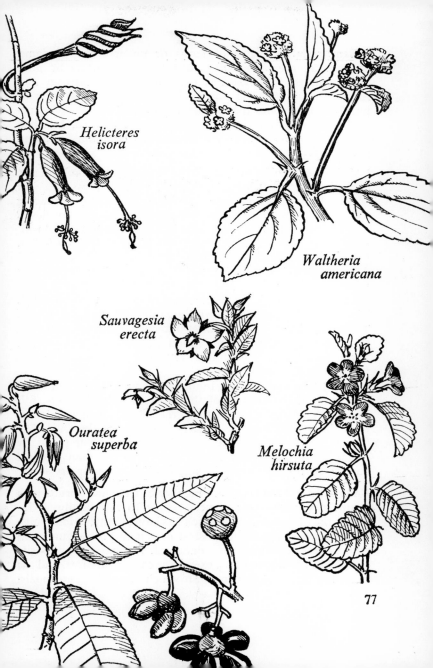

Helicteres isora

Waltheria americana

Sauvagesia erecta

Ouratea superba

Melochia hirsuta

77

Sauvagesia. A genus of herbs or undershrubs of damp ground. *Sauvagesia erecta* (illustrated), with white or pink flowers in the leaf axils, is common to both African and American tropics. The flowers have a conspicuous ring of purplish staminodes (barren stamens) and the capsule is surrounded by leafy sepals. The leaves have divided, hair-like stipules at the base. It is a small herb common on damp grassy places.

FAMILY DILLENIACEAE. In this family of woody plants and climbers the flowers are simple, with all parts free and arranged spirally. The ovary is superior, usually producing follicle fruits, but in the genus **Dillenia** the sepals become fleshy and surround the true fruit, giving rise to a large fleshy 'fruit' which may be as big as a grape fruit. That of *Dillenia indica*, Chalta, is edible. It is often cultivated.

Tetracera is a genus of climbing or scrambling shrubs with white or cream flowers and alternate rough leaves. As in other genera of the family the lateral veins of the leaves are parallel. The terminal panicles of flowers are followed by capsular fruit. The seeds have pretty, scarlet-branched outgrowths, called arils. The genus is chiefly found in America and Africa. *Tetracera asperula* (illustrated) is common in sandy places where there is open scrub.

Davilla is a mainly West Indian genus with leaves and stems like the last, but clusters of showy small yellow flowers, followed by capsules in which two of the sepals, which were larger than the others, become leathery and protect the fruit. The flowers are fragile and have usually dropped their petals by midday. *Davilla aspera* (illustrated) is a common tropical American species, usually in hilly districts on poor dry soil.

FAMILY GUTTIFERAE. A number of trees and shrubs with beautiful waxy-looking flowers belong to this family. It includes the Mammee Apple which has large, fleshy, edible fruits. Most plants of the family possess orange or yellow gum resin which oozes out if the stem is damaged. The leaves are opposite and thick. The flower parts, except the carpels, are free, and the calyx has bracts close beneath it which resemble extra sepals.

78

Tetracera asperula

Davilla aspera

79

The stamens are numerous, and the petals five or more in number. Oil glands, appearing as translucent dots, are found on the leaves. The most interesting genus is **Clusia**, which is entirely American, and very characteristic of certain types of forest. They mostly grow as shrubs or trees *on* other trees, but are not parasitic. Clasping roots attach the plant, and long hanging aerial roots may reach the forest floor, or dip in a river. The fruit is a large fleshy capsule. *Clusia colorans* is illustrated in colour, p. 101, Fig. 2.

FAMILY BIXACEAE. This is a very small family of trees and shrubs all belonging to the one genus **Bixa**. The plants have coloured juice. The leaves are alternately arranged, with palmate nerves, and stipules at the base. The flowers are regular and showy, borne in panicles, and with five petals and five sepals. There are numerous stamens, and the ovary, made of two carpels, is superior. The fruit is a capsule, opening to disclose seeds covered with red pulp. *Bixa orellana* (illustrated) is a tropical American shrub or small tree widely introduced to other parts of the tropics for the production of the red vegetable dye Annatto. The flowers are pinkish lilac, and the capsules are yellow, covered with stiff bristles. The seed is covered with bright red pulp, which is the source of the dye, and which is used by the American Indians to adorn their bodies.

FAMILY COCHLOSPERMACEAE. This is another small tropical family, the members being trees, shrubs, or small woody plants with thick underground stems. Like the previous family, they contain a coloured juice. The flowers, borne in racemes, are very showy, and rather resemble those of the last family, having five sepals, five petals, and numerous stamens, but the fruit is a capsule of three to five valves, and the seeds are not surrounded by pulp, but are sometimes covered with woolly hairs. The chief genus is **Cochlospermum**, a genus with large, usually yellow flowers, which tends to inhabit dry savannahs and semi-deserts. The genus is found on both sides of the Atlantic, some of the American species growing into tall timber trees, others being shrubs with rather stout, fleshy stems and thick underground parts which store water. They often

Cochlospermum vitifolium

Bixa orellana

lose their leaves in the dry season, and withstand repeated burning by growing again from the perennial rootstock. *Cochlospermum tinctoria*, a native of Africa, produces a yellow dye. *Cochlospermum vitifolium* (illustrated) is a tropical American species which may grow into a tree in dry savannah regions.

FAMILY FLACOURTIACEAE. This family, mostly consisting of trees and shrubs, was formerly included in *Bixaceae*. It differs in the flowers (often unisexual), in the leaves, which are usually pinnately veined, and not lobed, in the stamens, the anthers of which open by slits to set free the pollen, and not by pores, and in the fruit, which is usually a berry. There are numerous genera, many of which are trees, with rather insignificant flowers. The genus **Oncoba** has showy flowers. The plants are shrubs with sharp spines. *Oncoba spinosa* (illustrated) is a shrub with scented white flowers which have golden anthers. The flowers are followed by round berries about two inches across, which turn yellow when ripe. It is a native of Africa, but has been introduced to many places as a garden plant.

FAMILY PASSIFLORACEAE, the Passion Flower family. Most members of this family are climbing plants with tendrils. The leaves often have glands on the stalks, and are simple, entire, or lobed. The best known genus is **Passiflora,** which is easily recognized by the peculiar form of the flower. It has five petals and five sepals, which spread wide open. Within these is a conspicuous ring of thread-like outgrowths, the corona. Next come four or five stamens adhering at the base to a stalk (gynophore) which bears the ovary. This ovary bears three styles with rounded stigmas. The name 'Passion Flower' was given in allusion to incidents connected with Our Lord's Passion, the stigmas being supposed to represent three nails, and the corona a crown of thorns. The fruit of several species are eaten. *Passiflora quadrangularis* is the Granadilla. *Passiflora laurifolia* (illustrated in colour, p. 34, Fig. 3) is the Water Lemon, Simatoo, or Belle Apple. Many species are high climbers of tropical forests, with bright pink, blue, or scarlet flowers. Another species, *Passiflora foetida*, is a common weed in most parts of the tropics, especially in sandy places. The

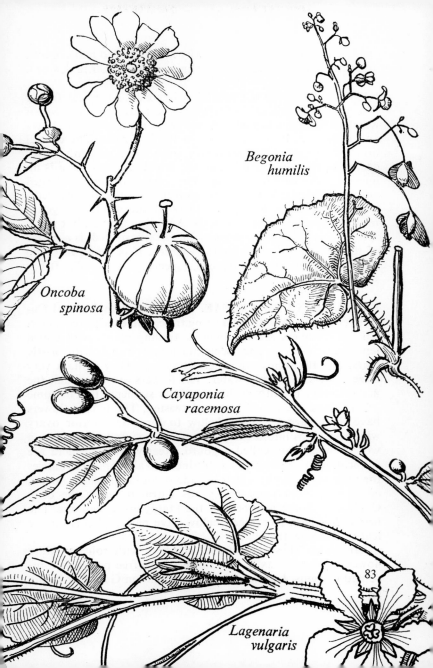

Begonia humilis

Oncoba spinosa

Cayaponia racemosa

83

Lagenaria vulgaris

small white flowers are enclosed by much divided hairy bracts, and the whole plant bears sticky hairs with a rather rank smell.

FAMILY BEGONIACEAE. This interesting tropical family has only four genera, much the largest and best known of which is the genus **Begonia**. In this genus the flowers are showy and unisexual, borne in cymes in the leaf axils. The central flower is usually male, with two large outer perianth leaves enclosing two smaller ones. In the female flowers there is an inferior ovary with three wings. The stigmas are much enlarged and convoluted. The seed capsule opens by pores, and the seeds, which are minute, are blown away by the wind. The genus *Begonia* is best represented in the American tropics, but many species occur in Africa. *Begonia humilis* (illustrated) is a native of the West Indies and South America. It is found in damp shady places in forested regions, especially in the hills. It has small pink flowers.

FAMILY CUCURBITACEAE. This is the Pumpkin and Cucumber family. It is an interesting tribe, and easy to recognize. All the members are climbing or trailing plants with coiled tendrils. The leaves and stems are usually rough with bristly hairs, and the stems are generally ridged. They contain very large vessels to convey water. The flowers are unisexual, the male flowers primitively having three stamens, but in some genera these are much bent and twisted. The female flowers have three carpels, joined below to form an inferior ovary which develops into a berry or a very large fleshy fruit with a woody outer wall, called a gourd. Nearly all the genera are tropical, many having been introduced to all tropical countries for their edible fruit, which include pumpkin, squash, melon, cucumber, and others. The genus **Citrullus** yields the drug Colocynth. Some members of the family are poisonous. The first two genera mentioned below have paired glands on the leaf stalk below the blade.

Lagenaria. These are annual climbers with solitary white flowers in the leaf axils. The flowers have free petals with indented margins. *Lagenaria vulgaris*, Common Gourd or White

84

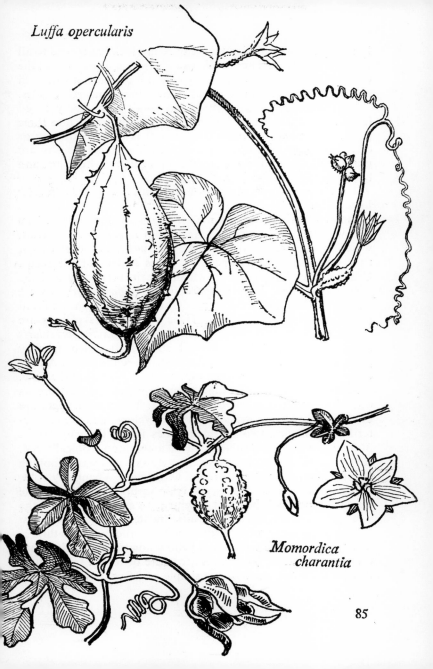

Luffa opercularis

Momordica charantia

Pumpkin (illustrated), is a native of Asia which has spread to all tropical countries. The fruit is usually long and swollen at the end, but is very variable. When young it is edible, but when old it is hard and woody, and used for making various receptacles.

Cayaponia. A genus with joined petals and deeply lobed leaves. The fruits are very small, and divided inside into three parts. *Cayaponia racemosa* (illustrated) is a small trailing or climbing plant of waste sandy places. The small flowers are green, and the small egg-shaped fruit is yellow when ripe, and becomes hard and woody.

The remaining genera mentioned do not bear glands on their leaf stalks.

Luffa. In this genus the male flowers are in racemes. The yellow petals are completely free, as in *Lagenaria*. The fruit, which is egg-shaped or oblong, becomes very fibrous as it ripens, and sometimes opens by pores to let out the seeds. Other species have fruits in which the tip rots away and the seeds shake out. *Luffa cylindrica* and *Luffa acutangula* are natives of the Old World tropics which have been naturalized in nearly all tropical places. Their dried fruit skeletons are called Loofahs, and are used like sponges. *Luffa opercularis* (illustrated) is a wild species with small fruit which open by pores when ripe. Notice that the tendrils are branched. All the other genera mentioned have joined petals, at least at the base.

Momordica is an interesting genus in which the fruit breaks open by three fleshy valves when ripe. The male flowers are borne in racemes, as in *Luffa*; they are yellow, and are characterized by having two or three scales inside the calyx tube. *Momordica charantia* (illustrated) is a common tropical weed. It is a slender vine with pretty yellow flowers and warty-looking pointed fruit which turn orange when ripe. When they split, they expose several black seeds lying in bright red pulp. The leaves are deeply lobed and indented. In cultivated forms the young fruit, which has a rather bitter taste, is cooked in curries.

Two genera with berry fruit may be mentioned. **Melothria** is a very slender vine with small yellow flowers and fruit about the size of cherries. The leaves are entire or lobed. In the male flowers the three stamens are simple and free. Several species

Coccinia indica

Melothria
guadelupensis

are weeds of both American and African tropics. *Melothria guadelupensis* (illustrated) resembles a tiny cucumber plant, with smooth round fruit which are black when ripe. Other species have red fruits.

Coccinia is another genus with berry fruits, easily distinguished by the male flowers in which the anthers are aggregated into a head, and the filaments of the stamens are joined into a column. The flowers are fairly large and showy. *Coccinia indica* (illustrated), originally from India, is now found wild in many countries. The flower is white, and the fruit, as big as a hen's egg, is scarlet.

Cucumis. This is the genus which includes the Cucumber (*Cucumis sativus*). The genus is recognized by having almost free petals, the male flowers having outgrowths at the tops of the anthers. The leaves are rounded or lobed. *Cucumis melo* is the Musk Melon. *Cucumis anguria* (illustrated) is the Brazilian Cucumber or Prickly Gherkin. It has yellow fruit as big as hens' eggs, covered with prickles, which are pleasant to eat if picked young. It is a common weed in some tropical places.

Cucurbita is the genus which includes the Pumpkin (*Cucurbita pepo*) and Vegetable Marrow. In this genus the flowers have a funnel-shaped calyx and large yellow corolla with the free petals about the same length as the corolla tube. The fruit is hairy. The leaves are rounded or slightly lobed, and the tendrils are branched. The fruit grows to a very large size. This species has been naturalized in nearly all parts of the tropics. The stamens have their anthers much twisted.

Citrullus. To this genus belongs the Water Melon (*Citrullus vulgaris*) (illustrated). Native of America, it has spread to all parts of the tropics. In this genus the male flower has a very short calyx, and the petals are almost free. The leaves are deeply lobed. The fruit is large and smooth, green outside and rose red inside, with black seeds. The flowers are yellow.

Benincasa. This is a genus with flowers like the last but with a thick cylindrical fruit which is covered with bristly hairs and coated with white wax. The leaves are entire. *Benincasa cerifera*, Wax Gourd or Chinese Pumpkin (illustrated), has a whitish fruit which is edible when cooked. It is a native of eastern Asia

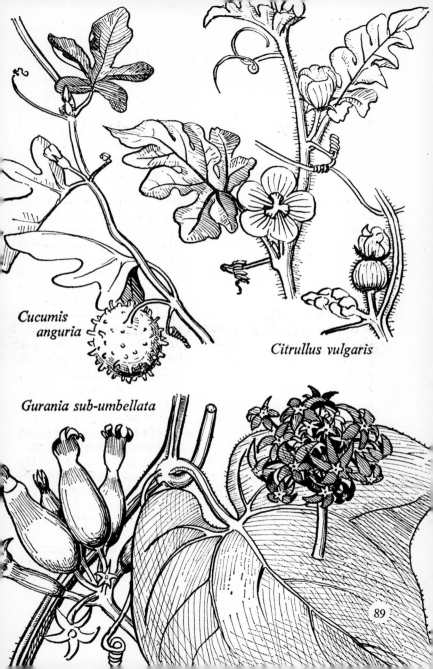

Cucumis anguria

Citrullus vulgaris

Gurania sub-umbellata

89

and Australia, but has been introduced to many other parts.

The genus **Gurania**, which is found only in tropical America, should be mentioned, as it has stinging hairs. It is a high climber of open forest. *Gurania sub-umbellata*, Blister Vine (illustrated), has orange flowers in close heads. Some of the flowers are male, and some female. The fruit is an orange berry. The leaves of this plant are heart-shaped, and the tendrils are unbranched.

FAMILY TURNERACEAE. This is a very small family found only in tropical Africa and America. It contains trees and shrubs as well as herbs. They have alternate leaves with the flowers solitary in their axils. The flowers are regular, with their petals and sepals free, arranged in fives. There are five stamens and three united carpels which later form a capsule. The three styles are free. Much the largest genus is **Turnera**, of which there are more than a hundred species. They occur in America, most of them being herbs with yellow flowers which grow on savannahs. *Turnera trioniflora* (illustrated) shows the characteristics of the genus well. The flower stem adheres in development to the leaf stalk, so that it appears to arise from the leaf. It has bright yellow flowers, and grows up to two feet high.

FAMILY CACTACEAE. This large and interesting family is entirely American except for the genus *Rhipsalis*, which is found also in Asia and Africa. No attempt, therefore, can be made to mention the many genera, and various books are available in which they are described, since members of nearly every genus are in cultivation. Besides *Rhipsalis*, to be described below, several other genera have been introduced and have become naturalized in the tropics and sub-tropics. The best known of these is **Opuntia**, Cochineal Cactus or Prickly Pear, which has become a pernicious weed in several places. Members of the Cactus family can be distinguished by the entire absence of leaves except in **Pereskia** and on the young stems of *Opuntia*. The stems are green and fleshy, and at the nodes they bear little cushions of hairs, often mixed with hooks and long spines. The spines at the base of each cushion apparently represent a leaf, and the rest represent an axillary shoot. From these cushions the large and showy flowers arise.

90

Benincasa
cerifera

Turnera trioniflora

Rhipsalis
cassytha

91

The flowers have all their parts numerous and arranged spirally. The carpels are sunk in the fleshy receptacle and later form a fleshy fruit. No Cactus has milky juice. This is a distinction from *Euphorbiaceae* and *Asclepiadaceae*, some members of which are cactus-like in form. In the genus **Rhipsalis** the stems are much branched and cylindrical. The flowers are small, and the fruit is a small berry. *Rhipsalis cassytha* (illustrated) grows as an epiphyte on trees. It has small insignificant flowers, in contradistinction to most other genera. The berries are white and translucent, with small black seeds.

FAMILY COMBRETACEAE. This is a family mainly of woody plants. It includes a number of woody forest climbers or lianas, and some seashore plants which belong to mangrove associations. To this family belongs the tropical Seaside Almond tree (**Terminalia**). The members of the family are distinguished by their opposite, entire leaves without stipules, and their racemes of flowers with inferior ovaries, followed by woody or drupe fruits, usually with wings. The flower parts are in multiples of four, or five.

In the largest genus, **Combretum,** the corolla is short and the stamens are long, and often brightly coloured. The fruits are angled or winged. Most of the members of the genus are climbers, shrubs or trees. Various species are found all over the tropics except in Australasia. *Combretum cacoucia* (illustrated) is a high climber of the riverside in South America. Its scarlet flowers are followed by poisonous five-sided fruits which are sometimes used to treat bat bites.

In the genus **Quisqualis** the flowers have a very long calyx tube, and the petals are large and showy. The flower parts are in fives, and the five-sided fruit opens to let out the seeds. *Quisqualis indica* (illustrated) is a climbing shrub, native to Asia and Africa but introduced and naturalized also in the American tropics. The flowers open white or pale pink, and gradually change to red.

Laguncularia is a shrub or small tree of mangrove swamps, with inflorescences of small white flowers followed by fruits with two wings. *Laguncularia racemosa*, White Mangrove (illustrated), is found on muddy coasts on both sides of the

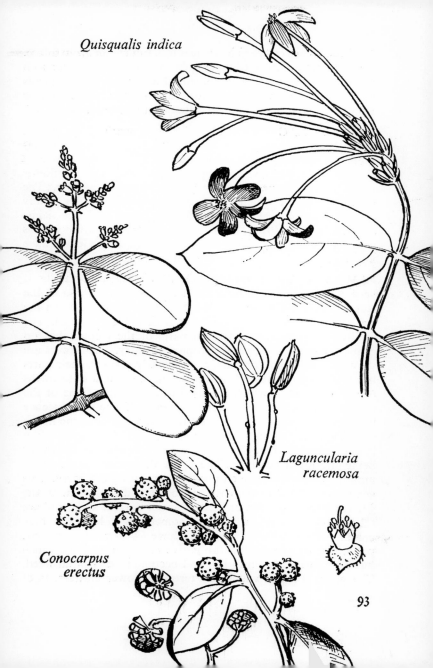

Quisqualis indica

Laguncularia racemosa

Conocarpus erectus

93

Atlantic. It flowers when a few feet tall, but can grow to a tree.

Conocarpus, Button Mangrove (illustrated), is another shrub of salty places. It is easily recognized by its tight round heads of small flowers without petals, followed by heads of tiny woody fruits. It has similar distribution to the last.

FAMILY ONAGRACEAE. In this family nearly all the genera are herbs. They mostly live in marshy places or in water, the commonest tropical genus being **Jussiaea.** In this genus the ovary is inferior, joined to the tubular calyx tube, and the flower parts are in fours. The flowers are generally yellow. The fruit is a capsule which opens by slits down the sides. Many species are common weeds of marshy places and rice fields. *Jussiaea nervosa,* Primrose Willow (illustrated), is a tall species common in swampy places in South America. The leaves have well-marked raised veins on the back.

FAMILY MELASTOMACEAE. This interesting family is very easy to recognize because of the peculiar veining of the leaves. There are three or more main veins running down the leaf, joined by cross-veins to give a netted appearance. The family is common in nearly all parts of the tropics, but no genus is represented in every tropical country. The flowers are showy, usually pink or purple, and nearly regular, their parts being in fours or fives. Their stamens have peculiar outgrowths of various shapes, which are used to distinguish some of the genera, and they are folded inwards in bud. The inflorescence is some form of cyme, which is either terminal or borne in the axil of one of the opposite leaves. One leaf of a pair is often larger than the other. The fruit is a berry or capsule, the ovary being inferior or nearly so. The genus **Melastoma** means 'black mouth', a condition which results from eating the berry. This genus is confined to the eastern tropics and Australia. In the genus **Clidemia** the flower clusters are in the leaf axils, and are followed by berries, which are sometimes a beautiful blue colour. *Clidemia hirta,* Koster's Curse (illustrated in colour, p. 68, Fig. 4), is a small shrub native to South America which has been introduced into Fiji and become a pestilential weed. The genus **Tococa,** which has terminal flower clusters, is of

94

*Combretum
cacoucia*

*siaea
vosa*

*coca
stata*

95

extreme interest because it produces special 'ant houses' or formicaria on its leaf stalks. *Tococa aristata* (illustrated) is common in the tropical forests of South America. Every leaf bears a formicarium, inhabited by a colony of minute ants.

FAMILY MYRTACEAE. A family of shrubs and trees with aromatic leaves. The leaves are opposite, and the flowers, which have free petals and very numerous stamens, have inferior ovaries. The fruit is a berry. Several well-known tropical fruit belong to this group, including the Guava, *Psidium guajava*. There are numerous species of this genus, some tiny shrubs and some fair-sized trees. They have cream-coloured, scented flowers, and many-seeded fruits. The cultivated Guava, *Psidium guajava* (illustrated), is frequently found wild as a shrub or small tree in bushy places. In the typical form the fruit is yellow, with pink flesh, and is strongly scented. Cloves belong to another related genus, **Eugenia.** The cloves of commerce are the buds, which are picked and dried before they open. *Eugenia jambos*, the Rose Apple, is cultivated in various parts of the tropics. The genus *Eugenia* is distinguished by having a fruit with one large seed instead of several small ones. Many species are known, all shrubs or trees.

FAMILY UMBELLIFERAE. This is a very easily recognized family, but poorly represented in the tropics. All the members are herbs with alternate leaves with sheathing bases, usually much divided, and umbels of small flowers with free petals and sepals and inferior ovaries. Many contain aromatic essential oil in the stems, leaves, and fruits. The tap root frequently becomes thick and stores food. To this family belongs the Carrot (*Daucus*.) The dry fruit in this family is also characteristic. It separates into two one-seeded pieces from below upwards. The only two common tropical genera are *Eryngium* and *Hydrocotyle*.

Eryngium. In this genus, which includes Sea Holly, the leaves are stiff, with toothed, prickly margins, and the flowers are in close heads, surrounded by an involucre of prickly bracts. *Eryngium foetidum*, Fit Weed (illustrated), is a small erect herb of waste ground, especially near houses. It has a rosette of simple leaves, and the flower-heads are greenish.

Psidium guajava

Eryngium foetidum

Hydrocotyle bonariensis

97

Hydrocotyle, Water Pennywort. This is a low herb of watery places, with minute heads of white flowers and shiny round (peltate) leaves. The leaves often grow so that the blade is vertical. *Hydrocotyle bonariensis* (illustrated) is found both in Africa and America.

FAMILY PLUMBAGINACEAE. A small family of herbs, undershrubs and climbers. The flowers are in spikes or heads; they are regular with joined petals, usually five in number, with the stamens opposite the petals (in most families they alternate with them). The ovary is superior.

Plumbago. This is the best known genus. The flowers are in spikes. The corolla has a very long tube, and the calyx, which is tubular, has sticky glandular hairs. The plants are bushy, or climbers. *Plumbago capensis*, a pale blue form, is commonly grown in gardens. *Plumbago scandens* (illustrated) is a common wild species with small white flowers.

FAMILY LOGANIACEAE. This is a family mainly consisting of trees and other woody plants. It includes **Strychnos**, a woody climber, one species of which is used to make the famous Curare arrow poison of the South American Indians. The genus **Spigelia** contains a principle which is used for killing intestinal worms. In this family the leaves are opposite or in whorls. The flowers are in umbel-like inflorescences; as a rule they have their petals and sepals in fours or fives, the petals being joined, and the ovary, usually of two carpels, is superior. There is one style. The fruit is a capsule. In the genus *Spigelia* the flowers are in terminal spikes. *Spigelia anthelmia*, Worm Grass (illustrated), is a common weed in towns, on cultivated ground and along waysides. It has pink flowers and warted fruits. The leaves are arranged in a whorl of four.

FAMILY GENTIANACEAE. This family is best known for the genus **Gentiana**, well represented in mountain floras of the temperate regions. There are a few rather specialized genera in the tropics, including some curious plants of forests which have no green leaves, and live in association with special fungi on

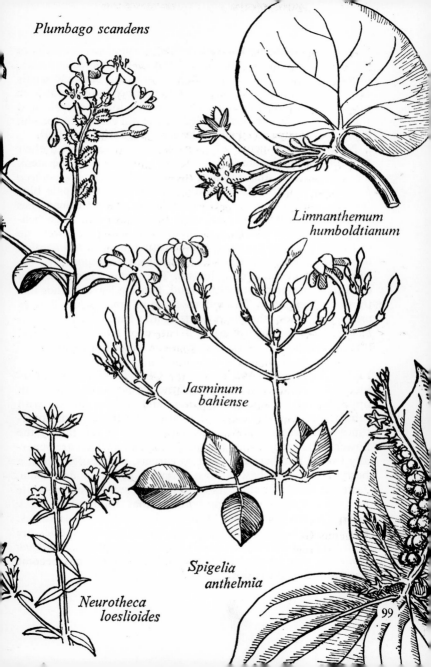

Plumbago scandens

Limnanthemum humboldtianum

Jasminum bahiense

Neurotheca loeslioides

Spigelia anthelmia

99

their roots. Nearly all are herbs with opposite leaves, which are entire and have no stipules. The flowers are arranged in cymes, and are regular with their parts in fours or fives. Petals and sepals are joined, and the stamens, equal in number to the petals, are attached to the corolla tube. There are two joined carpels, and the fruit is a capsule, surrounded by the old calyx and corolla. The ovary is superior. Few of the genera are widely spread.

Neurotheca. A genus of small branched herbs with their flowers solitary in the leaf axils and at the end of the stem. They are small and tubular, with four petals. *Neurotheca loeslioides* (illustrated) is a little annual weed with pale blue flowers, a weed of wet, sandy places. The genus **Chelonanthus** is American. The plants are erect perennials with large bell-shaped flowers in which the stamens all lie along the lower side of the corolla, but bent to touch a visiting insect. *Chelonanthus uliginoides*, Tropical Bluebell (illustrated in colour, p. 68, Fig. 2), has brilliant blue flowers. The genus **Limnanthemum** consists of water plants with round, floating leaves rather like those of *Nymphaea*. The inflorescence of small white flowers arises just below the short stalk of the leaf. *Limnanthemum humboldtianum* (illustrated) is a native of tropical America. Similar species are found in Africa and other hot regions.

FAMILY OLEACEAE. This is the Olive family. Most of its members are trees and shrubs of the temperate regions, with opposite, often compound, leaves, and regular flowers with tubular corollae and superior ovaries like the last, or sometimes with free petals. In many members of the family the flower parts are in fours, except the stamens, which are generally two in number, and the two carpels, which often form a berry fruit. The best known tropical genus is **Jasminum**, Jasmine: shrubs or climbers with star-like, sweet-scented, white or yellow flowers with long corolla tubes, followed by black berries which are divided into two lobes. The genus is best represented in the eastern tropics, but as several species are cultivated, they have been naturalized in many places. *Jasminum bahiense*, Star Jasmine (illustrated), for instance, has become naturalized in Barbados.

101

FAMILY APOCYNACEAE. This family resembles the last two, but its members always contain a milky juice, which may be poisonous, as in the well-known Oleander (*Nerium oleander*). They have opposite or whorled leaves with very regular lateral veins. The regular flowers are arranged in cymes, and have most of their parts in fives, the stamens being attached to the petals. The two carpels are usually joined by the style and free below, later producing capsules with hairy or winged seeds. The family contains trees, shrubs, herbs, and climbers.

Lochnera, Periwinkle. These are woody perennial herbs with showy flowers, and carpels which are free at the base and become follicle fruits. There are three species. *Lochnera rosea,* Madagascar Periwinkle (illustrated in colour, p. 101, Fig. 1), has been naturalized in all parts of the tropics. The flowers are white or pink, and the leaves shiny.

Rauwolfia. This genus has terminal inflorescences of small flowers, followed by berries. The berries are two-celled, with one or two seeds in each cell. *Rauwolfia canescens*, Devil's Peppers (illustrated), is a small shrub with whorls of leaves velvety hairy beneath, in the axils of which are small white flowers, followed by red berries. Various species are found throughout the tropics.

Tabernaemontana. Many plants formerly placed in this genus have now been placed in other genera, and the name is sometimes shortened to *Taberna*. They are shrubs with terminal cymes of white, star-shaped flowers with long corolla tubes, followed by two follicles. The leaves are opposite. *Tabernaemontana wallichiana*, Star Jasmine (illustrated), is a small shrub with shiny leaves and flowers resembling the true jasmine but without the fragrance. The fruit is a pair of orange-red follicles with red seeds. It is a native of India, and is cultivated as an ornamental plant, but has run wild in many places.

Allamanda. In this genus the flowers are large and handsome. They are cup-shaped and bright yellow. The plant is a woody climber with whorled leaves. The flowers are followed by conspicuous prickly capsules which contain winged seeds. Native to America, some species have been introduced to other parts of the tropics, especially *Allamanda cathartica*

103

(illustrated in colour, p. 102, Fig. 1), whose native habitat is riverside bush especially where the water is rather salt. An allied genus, common in the West Indies and South America, is **Mandevilla**. In this genus the fruit is a pair of long follicles with hairy seeds. *Mandevilla scabra* (illustrated) is a common twining plant of bushy savannahs in the American tropics.

Malouetia. In this genus the anthers, adhering to the stigma, stick out beyond the corolla. The plants are shrubs with small clusters of pink or white flowers followed by slender follicles with hairy seeds. *Malouetia schomburgkii* (illustrated) is a Guianese species with white, scented flowers. It is a slender shrub with dark stems.

FAMILY ASCLEPIADACEAE. Members of this family resemble the last in many features, including their opposite leaves and white milky latex. They can be distinguished by the interesting structure of the flower, which has special outgrowths from the petals (the corona) sometimes attached to the stamens, and the pollen is usually stuck together in glutinous masses called pollinia. The fruit, as in many of the *Apocynaceae*, is a pair of follicles, usually with hairy seeds. The flowers are in cymose arrangement, often reduced to a kind of umbel (all the stalks about the same length); they are regular, as in the last family, with superior ovaries. Plants in this family include many twining climbers, shrubs, and, especially in South Africa, fleshy forms superficially resembling Cacti.

Asclepias. In this genus the anthers with their pollinia, together with the corona, make a conspicuous head in the centre of the flower. The inflorescence is a kind of umbel. *Asclepias curassavica* (illustrated in colour, page 101, Fig. 5) is universal in the tropics; it is variously known as Silkweed, Milkweed, Redhead, and Bastard Ipecacuanha. It is a herb of waste grassy places, especially near the sea. It is said to be poisonous to stock. The seeds have long, silky hairs.

Calotropis. This genus resembles *Asclepias*, but the corona bears spurs beneath. *Calotropis procera*, French Cotton (illustrated in colour, page 101, Fig. 3), is a somewhat fleshy shrub with thick, soft shoots and hoary whitish leaves, which

104

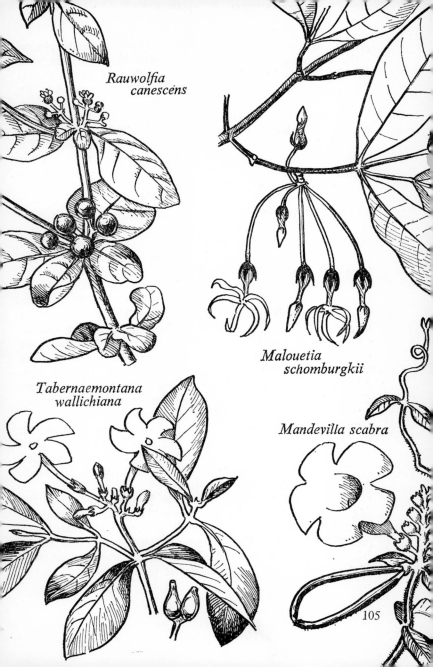

Rauwolfia canescens

Malouetia schomburgkii

Tabernaemontana wallichiana

Mandevilla scabra

105

grows ten feet tall. It is common in tropical waste places.

Sarcostemma. This is a plant of the Old World tropics, with clusters of *Asclepias*-like flowers on leafless green stems. *Sarcostemma viminalis* (illustrated) is an African species with greenish flowers, twining stems and rather slender fruit.

Funastrum is a rather similar genus confined to tropical America and the West Indies, in which the leaves are small and narrow, but not absent. *Funastrum clausum* (illustrated) is a climbing or trailing plant of salty places near the sea. It has umbels of pale greenish white flowers, and swollen follicles with hairy seeds like *Asclepias*.

FAMILY CONVOLVULACEAE. Nearly all the members of this family are twining plants with trumpet-shaped flowers and capsular fruits with four seeds. The leaves are alternate. There are very few shrubs or trees in the family. The flowers, which have their parts in fives, except their carpels, which are two in number, are arranged in cymes. The stamens, which are attached to the petals, are of unequal length. The best known tropical genus is **Ipomoea**, Morning Glory. The most important member of this genus is *Ipomoea batatas*, the Sweet Potato, which is now grown all over the tropics. The 'potatoes' are swollen roots from an underground stem. The genus *Ipomoea* is distinguished by its two-lobed stigma and prickly pollen. *Ipomoea biloba*, Goat's Foot Creeper (illustrated in colour, p. 67, Fig. 1), is a showy trailing plant with fleshy leaves and crimson-purple flowers, which occurs on sandy seashores.

The genus **Merremia** has the same characteristics as *Ipomoea*, but the pollen is smooth. *Merremia umbellata* (illustrated in colour, p. 101, Fig. 4) is a bright yellow-flowered twining climber found in waste places all over the tropics. The seeds are covered with short woolly hairs.

In **Quamoclit** the flowers resemble *Ipomoea* except that the stigma and stamens stick out of the flower instead of being shorter than the petals. *Quamoclit pennata* (illustrated) is a pretty annual twiner with finely divided leaves and bright crimson flowers. It is found wild in waste places in most parts of the tropics; it is apparently native to America.

Funastrum
clausum

Sarcostemma
viminalis

Evolvulus
nummularius

Quamoclit
pennata

107

Jacquemontia is a genus resembling *Ipomoea* but with the style cleft into oblong stigmas. Most are twiners with rather small blue or white flowers; the species *Jacquemontia evolvuloides* (illustrated in colour, p. 102, Fig. 2) is a herb with almost erect stems and leaves covered with silky whitish hairs.

Evolvulus. In this genus the flowers are wide open, almost saucer-shaped, and the stem does not twine. The flower has two forked styles. *Evolvulus nummularius* (illustrated) is a prostrate creeping plant, rooting at the nodes, which is common in many damp, grassy places. The flowers are white.

Aniseia. In this genus the flowers resemble *Ipomoea*, but the flowers have their two outermost sepals much larger than the others. The stigma has two rounded heads. *Aniseia martinicensis* (illustrated) is a twining climber with white flowers. It is common in grassy places all over the tropics.

Cuscuta. This genus is easily distinguished from all plants except *Cassytha* (p. 14) which it superficially resembles. The various species are known as Dodder, or Love Vine. They are parasitic plants with red or yellow stems and no leaves, attached to their hosts by suckers. Different species have different hosts. *Cuscuta americana* (illustrated) has yellow stems and close clusters of white, sweet-scented flowers, followed by capsules with four seeds.

FAMILY HYDROPHYLLACEAE. Members of this small family of herbs are found all over the world. They are distinguished by their usually hairy leaves without stipules, and their usually blue flowers arranged in compound inflorescences. The flowers have their sepals united and their petals also united to form a wheel-shaped corolla to which the stamens are attached. All parts are in fives except the two united carpels, which have separate styles. The ovary is superior, and becomes a capsule. The most obvious distinction from the previous family is that the seeds are numerous, instead of only four in a capsule. The plants never twine. The most widely spread tropical genus is **Hydrolea.** These are marsh herbs, with erect habit and blue flowers. Sometimes, as in *Hydrolea spinosa* (illustrated) there are thorns in the leaf axils. This and related species are

Cuscuta americana

Aniseia martinicensis

Hydrolea spinosa

Cordia cylindrostachya

109

sometimes found as weeds of rice fields and the sides of drainage canals, as well as in swamps.

FAMILY BORAGINACEAE. This family includes woody plants as well as herbs. The leaves are alternate, usually covered with rough hairs, and the regular flowers have all their parts except the carpels in fives, resembling the last family, from which all members are easily distinguished by the form of the carpels. The style is undivided below and usually arises from the base of the ovary. Although there are two carpels, the ovary is often divided across and appears to be made of four parts, each with one seed. The fruit is a hard nutlet, or a drupe.

In the genus **Cordia** the style is divided into four above, and the fruit is a drupe. The plants are shrubs or trees. *Cordia cylindrostachya*, Black Sage (illustrated), is a common West Indian shrub of waste ground, especially near the sea. It has white flowers and small red fruits. The greyish leaves have a strong aromatic scent.

Heliotropium, Heliotrope. In this genus the plant is a herb or shrub in which there is only one style. The spike-like inflorescences are coiled when young. The fruit is a drupe. *Heliotropium indicum*, Wild Clary (illustrated), is a species with rather broad leaves and white or pale mauve, scentless flowers. It is a common weed of waste ground in all parts of the tropics.

FAMILY VERBENACEAE. This family resembles the last, from which it can be distinguished by its opposite leaves, irregular flowers, and always capsule or berry fruits. Most members of the family are shrubs or trees, often with aromatic leaves. There are two or four stamens, the fifth not developing.

Lantana. A genus of hairy shrubs with strongly aromatic leaves and flowers in close heads of umbel form. The flowers have four stamens, and the fruit is a two-celled berry. *Lantana camara*, Sweet Sage (illustrated), is found throughout the tropics. The flowers open yellow, and change to bright pink. The berry fruit is black.

Lippia. In this genus the fruit is dry, and separates into two. The leaves are aromatic. *Lippia micromera*, Small Thyme (illustrated), is a small shrub grown in many parts of the

110

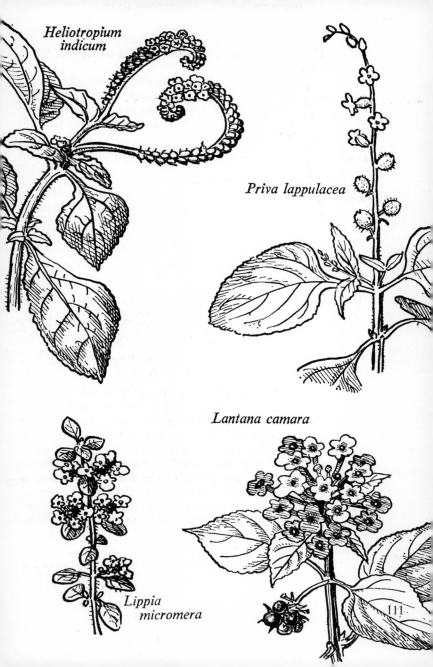

Heliotropium indicum

Priva lappulacea

Lantana camara

Lippia micromera

111

tropics as a herb for flavouring. It has close clusters of white flowers in the leaf axils.

In the genus **Priva** the flowers, in terminal racemes, produce prickly capsules enclosed in a calyx covered with sticky hairs. The leaves of some species are used as tea, and some have edible tubers. *Priva lappulacea* (illustrated) is a common tropical weed with pale blue flowers.

Avicennia. This is a genus of mangrove trees which grow on muddy tropical coasts. The white flowers are in axillary clusters; they are followed by velvety, olive-shaped fruits. *Avicennia nitida*, Olive Mangrove, Black Mangrove (illustrated), is a shrub or small tree with opposite, shiny leaves and small white flowers with four stamens and four corolla lobes. It is found on many muddy tropical coasts. In this genus queer erect roots emerge from the mud to enable the plant to get enough air. These are called pneumatophores. The olive-shaped fruits each contain a single seed in which the seed leaves are already green, and which begins to grow as soon as it falls in the sea.

Clerodendron. This is a widely distributed genus of shrubs and woody herbs with showy flowers in cymose inflorescences. The flower has a long corolla tube and five petals, the stamens project, and when they are ripe the style and stigma are bent down out of the way. Afterwards the stamens roll up and the style takes their place. The fruit is fleshy-looking, and divides into four parts. It eventually becomes a dry fruit, which is often dark blue, surrounded by the showy, persistent calyx. In *Clerodendron thompsonae* (illustrated in colour, p. 102, Fig. 3) the calyx is white, and the corolla dark red. A native of Africa, it is widely planted in tropical gardens.

Stachytarpheta. This is a genus of blue-flowered herbs with deep fleshy roots and spikes of flowers with only two stamens. The dry fruits are sunk into notches on the spike. *Stachytarpheta jamaicensis* (illustrated) is an erect herb often growing near the sea. It has shiny, rather broad, leaves with deeply serrated margins, and spikes of blue, or occasionally white flowers, which fall by the afternoon. It is common all over the tropics.

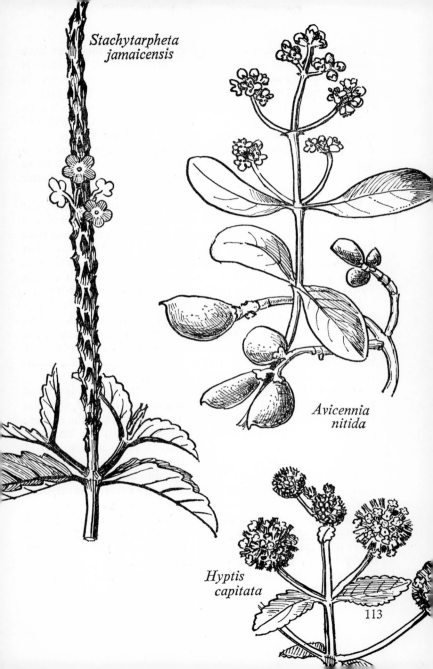

Stachytarpheta jamaicensis

Avicennia nitida

Hyptis capitata

113

FAMILY LABIATAE, the Mint family. All its members have aromatic essential oils and hairy opposite leaves. The stem is square, with the flower clusters in the leaf axils. The flowers are nearly always two-lipped, the petals being united to form a corolla tube and bearing two or four stamens. The sepals form a tubular calyx which persists to surround the fruit, a group of four nutlets. There are two carpels, the style arising as in *Boraginaceae*, from the base, and dividing at the tip into two stigmas. The plants are all herbs or shrubs, many of them having creeping underground stems. The family is much better represented in the temperate regions than in the tropics.

Leonotis. In this genus there are four fertile stamens, the lower pair being shorter than the upper one. The corolla is two-lipped, with the upper lip much longer than the lower one. The calyx is cup-shaped and has eight or ten teeth. Man Piabba, *Leonotis nepetaefolia* (illustrated), is an erect herb about four feet tall, with whorl-like inflorescences of reddish orange flowers. It is common on waste ground throughout the tropics.

Hyptis. In this genus the corolla is two-lipped with the lower lip abruptly bent down, and the calyx is five-toothed. *Hyptis capitata* is a common species with flowers in close heads, the individual flowers being white. The head bears an involucre of bracts below. In the West Indies this plant is used as a medicinal herb, and is called Lord Lavington.

Ocimum. In this genus the lower lip of the corolla is curved back, but not abruptly. The calyx is unevenly toothed, the lobe at the back being broader and more rounded than the others; the two in front being narrow and close together. The four stamens stick out beyond the corolla. *Ocimum sanctum*, Wild Basil, Mosquito Bush (illustrated), is a small shrubby herb with strongly aromatic leaves and insignificant greenish flowers, which is common in waste places in many parts. Several other species, all strongly aromatic, are used as herbs.

Coleus. In this genus the four stamens are more or less joined by their filaments. The calyx is two-lobed, five-toothed with the lower ones longer. Several species of *Coleus* are grown for their pretty leaves, which are variegated in red, green, and white. They are herbaceous plants, often with creeping stems, and

114

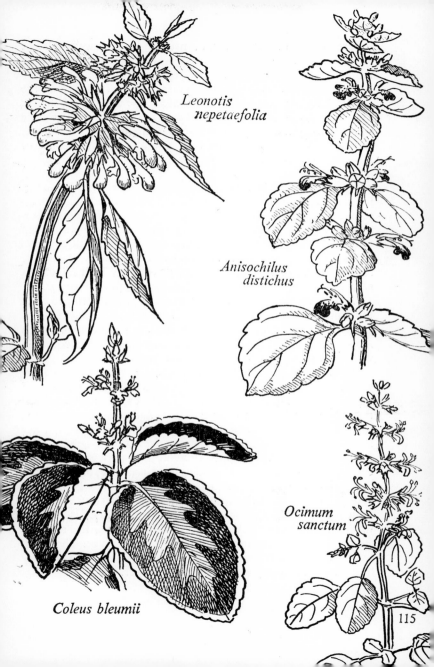

Leonotis nepetaefolia

Anisochilus distichus

Coleus bleumii

Ocimum sanctum

115

inflorescences of rather small, usually blue flowers. *Coleus bleumii*, Jacob's Coat (illustrated), is a common cultivated kind with blue and white flowers, native to Java.

Anisochilus. This genus resembles *Coleus* except that the stamens are only united at their bases. The teeth on the calyx are nearly equal. *Anisochilus distichus* (illustrated) is a common weed of rubbish dumps and waste places in many hot countries. It is an erect perennial herb with a terminal inflorescence of white flowers with crimson-purple lips.

FAMILY SOLANACEAE, the potato and tomato family. In this family the plants are all herbs or shrubs, some climbing, with alternate leaves. The flowers are nearly always regular, with a persistent calyx, and corolla of joined petals with stamens attached to the corolla tube alternately with the petals. The anthers sometimes open by pores. There are two carpels, joined, with a single style on top, and the fruit is a capsule or berry with numerous seeds. Many members of this family yield important drugs.

Datura. In this genus the flowers are trumpet-shaped, and the fruit is a four-valved capsule. The capsule is prickly. The genus yields the drug stramonium. *Datura stramonium*, Thorn Apple (illustrated), with white or mauve flowers, is a common weed of waste places throughout the tropics.

Nicotiana. A genus in which the pink or white flowers have very long corolla tubes and often open at night, closing up during the day. The fruit is a two-valved capsule. Members of this genus contain the drug nicotine. *Nicotiana tabacum*, the tobacco plant (illustrated), is an American species which has been introduced to all warm countries. It is a robust herb up to six feet tall, with pink or white flowers which have the calyx covered with sticky glandular hairs, and large broad leaves.

Capsicum. Members of this genus are the Red Peppers or Chillies. *Capsicum annuum* and *Capsicum frutescens* are commonly cultivated. *Capsicum minimum* (illustrated) is a small wild herb of bushy habit with greenish flowers, the stamens sticking out but opening by slits and not by pores. The small scarlet fruits are conical with short calyces. The fruit is very 'hot', and commonly known as Bird Pepper.

116

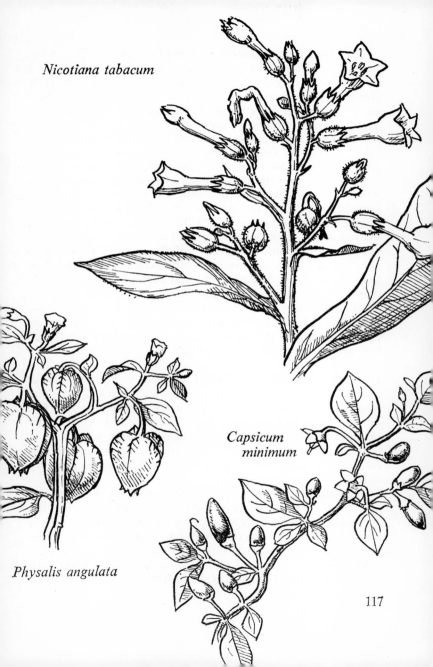

Nicotiana tabacum

Capsicum minimum

Physalis angulata

117

Physalis, Chinese Lantern or Cape Gooseberry. This genus has flowers resembling the last, but the fruit is enclosed in a large inflated calyx, which in some species becomes brightly coloured. *Physalis angulata* (illustrated) is a small annual herb often appearing on cultivated ground. The calyx remains greenish and the berry is purplish.

Solanum. This important genus includes a number of important food plants. *Solanum tuberosum* is the potato, a native of South America. *Solanum melongena* is the egg plant or aubergine. In this genus the anthers open by pores. The flower hangs with the anthers, which form a cone, facing downwards so that pollen can shake out through the pores. A similar arrangement is found in *Violaceae* (see p. 35). The flowers, with five petals, are yellow, white, or purple. The fruit is a berry, which in some species is poisonous, as are most of the green parts. Potatoes are stem tubers which grow in the leaf axils and develop below the ground. If exposed to the air and allowed to become green they too become poisonous. In spite of the fact that the green parts are usually poisonous, the leaves of *Solanum nigrum*, Black Nightshade (illustrated), which is found in varied forms all over the world are sometimes used as a pot herb or 'callalou'. The tomato, *Lycopersicum*, is closely allied to *Solanum*.

FAMILY SCROPHULARIACEAE. There are few useful plants in this family except some which yield drugs. The tropical species are mostly small shrubs or herbs, only a few of which can be mentioned here. They are characterized by their usually opposite leaves and irregular flowers, which usually have four stamens, and the fruit, which is a capsule with two carpels and numerous seeds, which never opens to the very base. The ovary is superior.

Capraria. Small shrubs with lanceolate, serrated leaves with flowers singly or in pairs in the leaf axils. In this genus the leaves are alternate. *Capraria biflora*, Goatweed (illustrated), is a widely distributed erect plant about two feet tall, with white flowers, usually in pairs, followed by small elliptical capsules.

Stemodia is a genus of tiny herbs a few inches high, with opposite leaves and clusters of small flowers in the leaf axils or

118

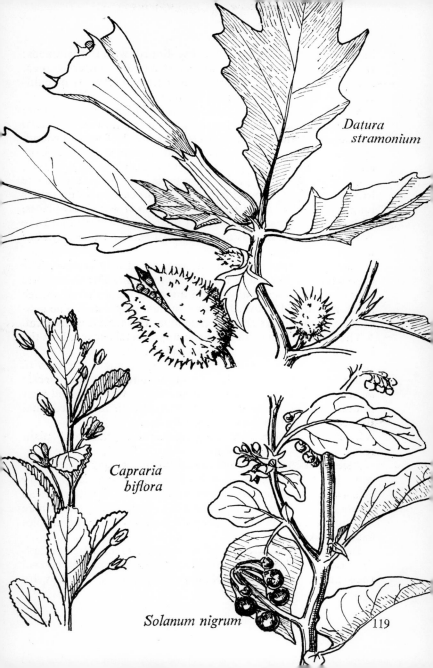

Datura
stramonium

Capraria
biflora

Solanum nigrum

119

in leafy racemes. The corolla is two-lipped, with four stamens; the petals of the upper lip are short and the flower is open. *Stemodia parviflora* (illustrated) is a tiny little weed of cultivated ground, with bluish purple flowers.

Vandellia is a rather similar genus in which the two lips are closely opposed closing the mouth of the flower. *Vandellia diffusa* (illustrated) is another creeping weed of waste ground, especially in the American tropics. Its flowers are white, borne singly in the leaf axils on very short stalks. The stem is square.

Conobia. Another genus of minute plants with opposite leaves very similar to the last, but with open flowers on rather long stalks. *Conobia aquatica* is a tiny herb of wet grassy places, with violet flowers. It is confined to tropical America and the West Indies. The stem is square, as in *Vandellia*. The calyx has five slender sepals.

Bacopa. In this genus the flowers are nearly regular. The calyx enlarges to enclose the developing fruit. The flowers are blue or white. *Bacopa aquatica* is a stouter plant than the three herbs mentioned above. It grows in marshy ground. The solitary, axillary flowers are very pale blue. The stem is cylindrical.

The next three genera have the upper petals covered by the lower ones in bud in contrast to the previous three.

Scoparia. This is a genus of small, erect, branched herbs with white flowers, the flowers having a four-lobed corolla. *Scoparia dulcis*, Sweet Broom, is a common weed of waste ground near houses in all tropical countries. It is said to have medicinal properties and its leaves are used for tea.

The next two genera are parasitic on grass and plant roots.

Alectra. Yellow-flowered erect herbs of grassy places. The calyx has five lobes and is five-ribbed. *Alectra melampyroides* (illustrated) is a hairy erect herb about a foot tall, with stalkless flowers in the leaf axils. The leaves have three main veins. There are about twenty other species found all over the tropics except in Australia.

Buchnera. This is a genus of slender, erect herbs of ill-drained acid, or very poor soils. The flowers have narrow corolla tubes and spreading petals of nearly equal size, followed by dry

120

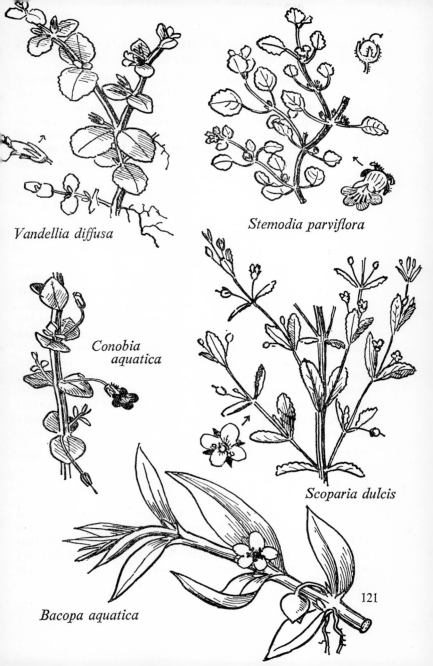

Vandellia diffusa

Stemodia parviflora

Conobia aquatica

Scoparia dulcis

Bacopa aquatica

121

capsules. *Buchnera rosea* (illustrated) is rather misnamed as the flowers are pale blue or white, not rose-coloured.

FAMILY LENTIBULARIACEAE. The members of this family are insectivorous plants of bogs and wet places. There are only two genera, of which the commonest is **Utricularia,** Bladderwort, of which there are over two hundred species. Some of the largest and most interesting ones live only in the pitchers of plants belonging to the pineapple family in South America. The insects and other tiny water animals are caught in the 'bladders', which are provided with a sort of trap-door arrangement allowing them to enter but not to leave. These bladders are borne, as a rule, on a branched green part of the plant under water, and these plants do not bear any organs which are true leaves. Other species, including the large South American ones mentioned, have true leaves as well. The flowers of all species are showy and usually brightly coloured. They are two-lipped, with the lower lip spurred, and they are borne in erect racemes. Each flower has two stamens and two carpels, the latter being joined and later producing a capsule with many small seeds. *Utricularia foliosa* (illustrated) is one of the commoner floating species with yellow flowers. It is found in slow-moving fresh water in both the Old and New Worlds. It is always found in acid, peaty water, and does not thrive where it is alkaline. Of the many other species which are found all over the world, some have yellow, others purple-white, blue, or pinkish flowers. Although their flowers in many ways resemble those of the last family, the peculiar characteristics of the vegetative parts make them easy to distinguish.

FAMILY PEDALIACEAE. This is another small family whose members closely resemble those of *Scrophulariaceae*. Its members are mostly shore and desert plants originally confined to the Old World, but one genus, **Sesamum,** Sesame, is economically important for its flat oily seeds, and has been introduced to all warm countries. In this family the leaves are always opposite, at least on the lower part of the plant, and bear glandular hairs. There are curious glands associated with the flowers which are formed from modified flowers. The fruit is a capsule

Buchnera
rosea

Utricularia
foliosa

Alectra
melampyroides

123

or nut, and the flowers closely resemble those of *Scrophulariaceae*. In *Sesamum* the tubular corolla has five petal lobes and four stamens attached to the corolla tube making two pairs, the anthers of which meet at the back of the flower. The capsule is rather hard and woody, and contains many flat, round seeds. *Sesamum radiatum* is illustrated in colour, p. 102, Fig. 5.

FAMILY GESNERIACEAE. The plants in this family are of little economic importance, but generally have showy flowers, and many are grown in gardens, the best known being the Gloxinia (**Sinningia**). The plants have, as a rule, fleshy, hairy, opposite leaves, and they usually grow in damp, shady spots. Those, like *Sinningia*, which have fleshy corms can withstand long dry periods. The flower structure in this family resembles that of the three families previously mentioned, being tubular with five petals and usually four stamens attached to the corolla. The easiest distinction is in the form of the fruit. When this is cut open it is seen that the seeds are attached to outgrowths (placentas) from the outer wall, and not from the centre as in the other families. The fruit is a capsule or berry.

Episcia. This is a New World genus of creeping plants increasing by runners. The leaves are usually large and hairy, with rather long stalks, and the flowers are in clusters in the leaf axils. The corolla is nearly regular, but has a sac-like nectary on the upper side at the base. The ovary is superior, and becomes a two-valved capsule with numerous seeds. *Episcia hirsuta* (illustrated) is a large-flowered species with white flowers tinged with purple on the outer part of the petals.

Codonanthe is an example of a genus of this family in which the fruit is a berry. The corolla is shaped like that of *Episcia*. *Codonanthe confusa* (illustrated) is an interesting South American fleshy prostrate plant with fleshy, hairless leaves, which grows as an epiphyte on trees, and is nearly always associated with an ants' nest. The flowers are white, and the fruit is a showy scarlet berry.

Saintpaulia. This genus is best known for the African Violet, *Saintpaulia ionantha* (illustrated in colour, p. 102, Fig. 4). It is a native of the East African tropics, but is grown all over the

124

Episcia hirsuta

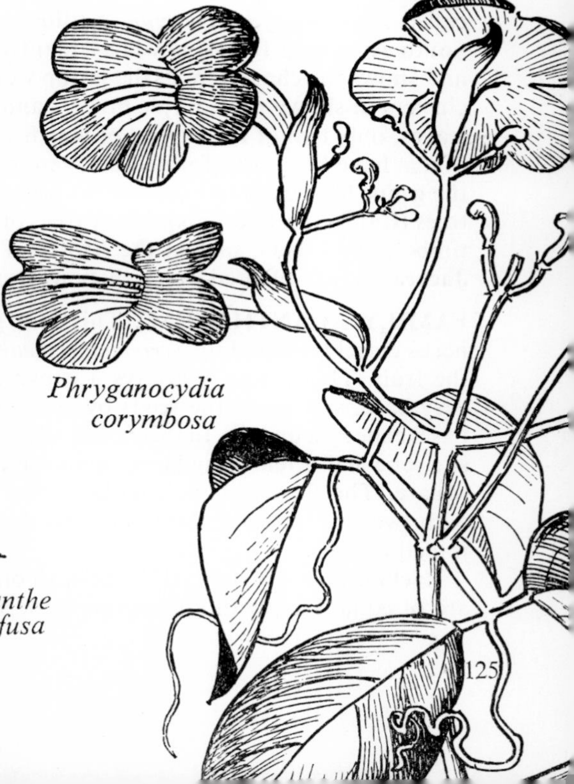

*Phryganocydia
corymbosa*

*Codonanthe
confusa*

125

world as a house plant. The corolla has spreading violet petals and the showy yellow stamens protrude from the flower. The stigma is bent either to the right or to the left. This plant can be propagated by its fleshy leaves.

FAMILY BIGNONIACEAE. This family agrees with *Gesneriaceae* in nearly all its other characters, but the plants usually have compound leaves. The family also differs in having all its members woody, trees, shrubs, or tropical forest climbers. To this family belongs the curious West Indian Calabash Tree (**Crescentia**) which produces enormous fruits as big as footballs, with a hard outer woody covering and a soft, pulpy interior, which are used for making useful pots and basins. The only genus common to both the Old and the New Worlds is **Catalpa**, a showy flowering tree. The original genus **Bignonia** has now been split up into a large number of smaller genera on differences of flower and fruit structure. *Bignonia magnifica*, now called *Phryganocydia corymbosa* (illustrated), a native of the South American forest, is widely planted in tropical gardens, and shows the characters of the group well. It has large cymose clusters of showy rose-purple flowers and pinnately compound leaves, only two of the leaflets of which are green and flat. The others have been transformed into tendrils. Other members of the genus have claw-like tendrils which can cling to the bark of trees (Cat's-claw Creepers). Many trees of the family are useful timber, and others, such as the African Tulip Tree, **Spathodea, Jacaranda,** are planted everywhere as ornamental plants.

FAMILY ACANTHACEAE. This is a genus of shrubs and herbs closely resembling *Scrophulariaceae* but distinguished by the fruit. This is nearly always a capsule which opens to the very base, and ejects the seeds by curious outgrowths at their bases called jaculators. In this family the leaves are always opposite, one leaf often being larger than the other, and the stem is square. The flowers have tubular, often two-lipped corollas, with two or four stamens attached to them, and the usual two joined carpels.

   Ruellia. This is a genus of herbs with blue flowers. The leaves are of equal size, with inflorescences or single flowers in their

126

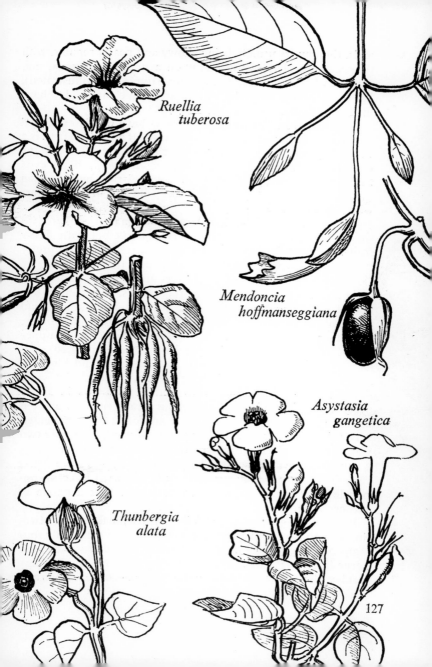

Ruellia tuberosa

Mendoncia hoffmanseggiana

Thunbergia alata

Asystasia gangetica

127

axils, the flowers usually being showy and nearly regular, with four stamens. The capsules contain a number of seeds, and explode when damp. *Ruellia tuberosa*, Minnie Root (illustrated), has swollen roots at the base of the stem which are said to have medicinal value.

Thunbergia. In this genus the flowers have widely expanded petals and the flowers are solitary in the leaf axils. The fruit is a beaked capsule with four seeds. The plants are often twining climbers with showy flowers. *Thunbergia alata*, Black-eyed Susan (illustrated), originated in tropical Africa, but has been introduced to all hot countries. It has yellowish orange flowers with black centres.

Mendoncia (American) and **Afromendoncia** (African) are two similar genera with flowers like *Thunbergia* but with fleshy fruits. *Mendoncia hoffmanseggiana* (illustrated) is a pretty twining climber with red flowers and black fruits.

Asystasia. In this genus the flowers are in spikes ending the main stem, with small bracts at their bases. The fruit is like that of *Ruellia*, and the form of the flower is similar, but in bud the petals of *Ruellia* are twisted regularly one over the other, whereas in *Asystasia* the lower petals are folded over the upper ones. *Asystasia gangetica*, Tropical Primrose (illustrated), is a native of India which has spread to tropical Africa and America. It is a creeping or semi-climbing plant with yellow or white flowers, sometimes flushed with mauve. It grows in shady damp places. Members of the genus **Eranthemum** are often used as ornamental shrubs, as there are forms with variegated leaves. In this genus the flowers are two-lipped, with only two stamens. The flowers are in terminal panicles, each flower having a calyx with five segments. The plants are shrubs from forest regions. *Eranthemum atropurpureum* (illustrated) has crimson-purple flowers and purplish bronze leaves. It is a native of Eastern Asia.

Barleria is a genus of low shrubs in which the flowers are two-lipped with two stamens as above, but the calyx has only four segments. The flowers have spiny bracts at their bases and are borne in the leaf axils. *Barleria lupulina* (illustrated) is a spiny shrub with narrow leaves and cone-like heads of reddish bracts

128

Eranthemum atropurpureum

Barleria lupulina

Beloperone guttata

Justicia ovata

Randia formosa

129

in the axils of which are orange-yellow flowers which open a few at a time. A native of Africa, it has spread to many other parts of the world where it is sometimes a pest in dry places.

Justicia. In this genus the two-lipped flowers have peculiar shaped stamens. There are only two, but the unequal positions of the anther lobes make them appear like four. The lower lip has three lobes. *Justicia ovata* (illustrated) has one-sided racemes in the leaf axils. The flowers are pinkish mauve with darker markings. It is a plant of damp, shady places.

Beloperone is a genus with similar flowers, but these are in the axils of large, showy bracts, and the stamens and style project slightly beyond the upper lip. *Beloperone guttata* (illustrated) is commonly known as the Shrimp Plant or Cockroach Plant because its overlapping reddish bracts remind one of the overlapping segments of a crustacean or insect, and the old stamens and styles resemble antennae. The flowers themselves are comparatively insignificant, white with dark purple spots. This plant is a shrub, native to the New World, which has been widely planted all over the tropics as an ornamental plant.

FAMILY RUBIACEAE. This family and the two following are distinguished by their flowers having inferior ovaries. It is a very large family indeed, but it contains comparatively few herbs. Nearly all members are trees and shrubs, including **Coffea,** Coffee, and **Cinchona,** the bark of which yields quinine. The family also contains many beautiful garden plants, such as **Gardenia** and **Ixora.** All members of this family have opposite leaves with stipules. The flowers are in cymose arrangements of many kinds, or sometimes solitary. The calyx often has minute sepals; the corolla, which is tubular, has four to six or more petals, and the same number of stamens attached to the corolla alternately with them. The two carpels are united to form a single ovary and style, with two separate stigmas or two lobes at the top. The fruit is a capsule, or a berry or drupe.

Randia. This is a genus of shrubs rather like *Gardenia.* The shrubs may be spiny. The flowers are large, and are solitary or a few together in the leaf axils. They are white or yellowish, with twisted petals when in bud. *Randia formosa* (illustrated) is

130

Sabicea glabrescens

Morinda
citrifolia

Mussaenda erythrophylla

Uncaria
africana

Cephaelis
barcellana

131

a shrub of ill-drained ground which has become established in many tropical areas. It has white, star-shaped flowers, the petals being green on the back, and they are sweetly scented at night. The fruit is an oval berry, yellow when ripe.

Uncaria. This is a genus of climbers with their flowers in close ball-like heads. They climb by means of pairs of hooked spines. *Uncaria africana* (illustrated) is an African species with yellow, silky-looking flowers. One species of this genus, *Uncaria gambier*, from Malaya yields a valuable tannin.

Mussaenda. In this interesting Old World genus one sepal becomes greatly enlarged into a coloured leaf. The flowers themselves are quite small and not showy. *Mussaenda erythrophylla* (illustrated) has the large sepal brilliant red. It is a common bush in Africa, and has been introduced to nearly all hot countries. There are other species with yellow sepals.

Sabicea. This genus of scrambling climbers is found in the tropics on both sides of the Atlantic. The flowers are in axillary clusters, followed by berries. The sepals are of normal size. *Sabicea glabrescens* (illustrated) is a South American species with small white flowers and red berries. There are about thirty other species.

Morinda. This is a very curious genus. The calyces of the white, tubular flowers are stuck together. When the fruit develops, the whole structure becomes enlarged and fleshy like a curious kind of pineapple. *Morinda citrifolia*, Yaw Bush (illustrated), is a native of India which has been introduced into the West Indies and South America as well as many parts of the Old World. Its waxy white flowers are followed by a greenish white fruit with a rather unpleasant smell.

Cephaelis. In this genus the flowers are in close heads which superficially resemble those of the next family, but can be easily distinguished from them by the fact that the youngest flowers are not always nearest the centre. The head is surrounded by bracts, which are often very brightly coloured. The fruit is drupe-like, and is often bright blue or white when ripe. The flowers are rather small, and are white or yellow. This genus is often united with another similar one, **Uragoga,** and some members are known by either name, while in other cases the

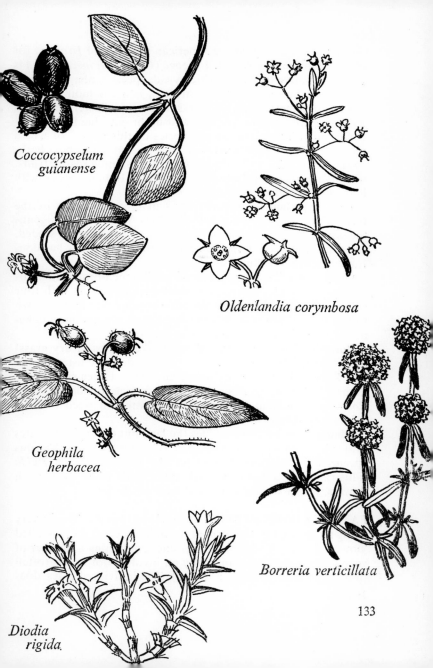

Coccocypselum
guianense

Oldenlandia corymbosa

Geophila
herbacea

Borreria verticillata

Diodia
rigida

133

name *Cephaelis* is used for American species and *Uragoga* for those from the Old World. *Uragoga* (*Cephaelis*) *ipecacuanha* is a species native to Brazil, which yields ipecacuanha. *Cephaelis barcellana*, Soldier's Cap (illustrated), is a common shrub of the South American forest. The small yellow flowers, enclosed by two scarlet bracts, are followed by bright blue fruits.

Geophila. There are fifteen species of this genus, of which about half are found in Africa. They are small creeping herbs of the forest floor with white flowers and shining scarlet fruits. *Geophila herbacea* (illustrated) is a West Indian species with hairy leaves and hairy fruits.

Coccocypselum is another genus of creeping herbs of the forest floor, but is confined to the New World. In this genus the tiny flowers are blue, and the berries, which are many seeded, are also blue. *Coccocypselum guianense* (illustrated) has conspicuous brilliant blue fruit.

Oldenlandia. This is a genus of small, much-branched herbs with small slender leaves and usually white flowers with four petals, followed by many seeded capsules opening by two valves. *Oldenlandia corymbosa* (illustrated) is a common ephemeral weed of cultivation all over the tropics.

Borreria. This is a genus of heath-like shrubs of dry grassland. The small white flowers are aggregated in clusters in the leaf axils and at the ends of the branches. Other species are herbs. The fruit is a small capsule which divides in two. *Borreria verticillata* (illustrated) is a common weed in both Africa and America.

Diodia. This genus resembles the last, but the fruit separates into two halves and does not open to let out the seeds. Various species are common throughout the tropics. *Diodia rigida* (illustrated) is a low savannah plant with white or pinkish flowers, tough woody stem, and hard rough leaves.

FAMILY COMPOSITAE. The Sunflower family. This is very easily recognized by the form of the inflorescence. The so-called 'flower' is really a special inflorescence containing a number of very small florets surrounded by an involucre of bracts (often thought of incorrectly as a 'calyx'). The individual calyx does

134

2

3

4

136

not develop as such. In the individual flowers the corolla usually has five joined petals. The five stamens are attached to these, and are *joined by their anthers*. There are two united carpels with free stigmas, and the ovary is inferior. It develops into a small, dry, achene fruit usually wrongly described as a seed, which is often dispersed by a hairy 'parachute' at the top, or by bristles or hooks. The outgrowths of the top of the ovary are called the 'pappus'; they are really the modified calyx of the individual floret. In some members of the family all the florets in a head are alike, and all complete. In others the outer florets are different. They may have irregular, strap-shaped corollas; then they are known as ray florets. They may be showy and barren, as in Gaillardia, but with regular corollas, and in one large section of the family, which includes the Sunflower (**Helianthus**) the outer ray florets are female or sometimes barren, and the inner disc florets are hermaphrodite. In another section of the family all the florets are irregular and strap-shaped (ligulate), and in this section the plant contains latex. This group is hardly represented in the tropics; it includes the commercially valuable Lettuce (**Lactuca**) and Chicory (**Cichorium**). Only a very few other members of the family are useful. Sunflowers are grown for the oil in their seeds, and one species, the 'Jerusalem' Artichoke (*Helianthus tuberosus*), is grown for its tubers. **Pyrethrum** is grown for the production of an insecticide, and many of the family are grown as ornamental plants. A few are pernicious weeds. None are trees.

In the six following genera the flowers are of two kinds, hermaphrodite disc florets and female ray florets. The receptacle bears scales with the florets in their axils, and the fruit do not have hairy pappus.

Synedrella. This is a genus of small herbs with hairy, opposite leaves and small yellow flowers. The achenes are of two kinds; the outer ones are winged, and the inner ones bear two or three bristles. *Synedrella nodiflora*, Yellow Starwort (illustrated), is a common weed of waste ground in the tropics.

Bidens, Spanish Needle, Spanish Nettle, Bur Marigold. In this genus of herbs the leaves are divided. The heads are yellow, or may bear white ray florets. The achenes bear two or more

137

stout bristles armed with reflexed barbs which catch in clothes or the coats of animals. *Bidens bipinnata* (illustrated) is an erect herb with yellow flowers followed by heads of achenes bearing four or five barbed bristles. It is a common weed of waste ground throughout the tropics. A similar but larger plant with less divided leaves and larger flower heads, sometimes with white ray florets, is *Bidens pilosa*. The achenes in this species have only two barbed bristles. It is nearly as common as the last species.

Wedelia. A genus with white or yellow daisy flowers and opposite simple or lobed leaves. The pappus on the achenes is in the form of a ring of a few bristles which soon fall off. *Wedelia trilobata*, Yellow Creeping Daisy (illustrated), is a common creeping plant with rough aromatic leaves and showy bright yellow flower-heads in the leaf axils. It is a native of tropical America which has spread to Africa.

Eclipta. In this genus the flowers are not very conspicuous. There are both ligulate ray florets and regular disc florets. The achenes are thick, and the few bristles are not arranged in a ring. *Eclipta alba* (illustrated) is a common herb of waste places and cultivated ground all over the tropics, with whitish flower-heads up to about half an inch across, and rather narrow, opposite leaves with serrated margins. It is an annual plant.

Aspilia. This genus resembles *Wedelia*, but the ray florets are not fertile. Some members of the genus are shrubby plants or woody herbs. They are found both in the Old and New Worlds. *Aspilia africana* (illustrated) is a yellow-flowered scrambling herb with rough leaves which are opposite and have three veins like those of *Wedelia*. The fruit has a ring of bristles.

Acanthospermum. There are several members of this genus which have become widely spread owing to the effective means of dispersal of the achene, which is covered with hooked spines. The flowers are yellow. *Acanthospermum hispidum*, Star Burr (illustrated), is an erect branched herb about two feet tall resembling *Synedrella nodiflora* except for its fruits. It is a widespread weed.

Emilia. In this genus the leaves are alternate and deeply indented near the base. The heads have all the florets alike and tubular. The fruit bears white, hairy pappus. The bracts

138

Bidens bipinnata

Synedrella nodiflora

Eclipta alba

Wedelia trilobata

139

surrounding the head are in a single series, not overlapping. *Emilia sonchifolia* (illustrated) is a common weed of waste places throughout the tropics. The tassel-like heads are mauve. An allied species, *Emilia coccinia*, Soldier's Tassel, has bright crimson heads. It is not so widely distributed as the former species.

Senecio. This is an enormous genus. Some species growing in the mountainous parts of East Africa grow into tree-like forms. Another species, a native of South Africa, grows like ivy. Some are fleshy like Cacti. *Senecio confusus* (illustrated) is a climbing species with brownish orange flower-heads in showy panicles, the individual heads being about an inch across, with large ray florets. The fruits have conspicuous white pappus, a characteristic of the genus ('Senex' is Latin for Old Man). In this genus the bracts surrounding the heads form a sort of false calyx below. There are about two thousand other species, some with, and some without ray florets.

Erigeron. This is another genus rather like *Senecio*, but well distinguished by the stiff, bristle-like pappus on the fruits. The flower-heads have very narrow ray florets, or are all tubular and the involucre bracts are long and narrow, with a series of small ones below. They are erect herbs, often annuals, with white, greenish, or mauve heads, and narrow unstalked leaves alternately arranged. *Erigeron bonariensis* (illustrated) and others occur as weeds of cultivation in many tropical countries and in warm temperate regions.

Vernonia. In this genus the flowers are all tubular, and the bracts surrounding the heads are in several series overlapping like scales. The flowers are blue, mauve, or white. The fruits are crowned with white pappus. *Vernonia cinerea*, Blue Fleabane (illustrated), is an erect, much-branched annual about two feet tall, with heads of blue flowers. It is a common weed of cultivation all over the tropics.

Elephantopus, Elephant's Foot. This genus resembles Vernonia except that the flower-heads are over-topped by leafy bracts. *Elephantopus scaber* (illustrated) is a common perennial weed of waste ground in all hot countries. The lower leaves make a spreading rosette, and the branched inflorescence has heads of small mauve or white flowers, all tubular.

Aspilia africana

Emilia
sonchifolia

Acanthospermum
hispidum

Senecio confusus

141

Sparganophorum. This is a genus which could be mistaken for *Elephantopus*, but the fruits have no pappus at all. The heads of mauve flowers are sessile in the leaf axils. *Sparganophorum vaillantii* (illustrated) is a herb about two feet tall, found in damp grassy places in semi-shade. It is found in both the Old and New Worlds.

Eupatorium, Hemp Agrimony. The members of this genus have numerous small heads of flowers resembling those of *Vernonia*, but the anthers of the stamens have outgrowths at the apex. The fruit has pappus like *Vernonia*. The leaves are alternate. *Eupatorium odoratum*, Christmas Bush (illustrated), is a semi-shrub, very common in warm parts of America. The flowers are white or mauve-pink.

Mikania. This is a genus of twining climbers with panicles of small heads of tubular white flowers like those of *Eupatorium*. The leaves are opposite. *Mikania micrantha*, Bitter Tally (illustrated), grows in similar places to the last. The genus is found in both America and Africa, but there is only one African species, *Mikania scandens*.

Ageratum. The cultivated species of this genus, *Ageratum mexicanum*, is a well-known garden flower, with blue, sweet-scented tassel-like heads and opposite leaves. *Ageratum conyzoides* (illustrated) is similar with smaller flowers and is found in all tropical countries as a weed of cultivation. It is easily distinguished from *Vernonia cinerea*, which it otherwise resembles, by its opposite leaves and absence of pappus on the fruits, which are crowned with five minute scales.

Tridax. This is an American genus which has spread widely to other tropical regions. The flowers are in solitary conical heads with overlapping bracts, the central ones being regular and the outer ray florets, which are few in number, broadly strap-shaped. The leaves are opposite and three-lobed. The pappus on the fruit is feathery, and brownish white. *Tridax procumbans* (illustrated) has cream-coloured ray florets and yellow disc florets. It is a common wayside weed with short, tufted, creeping stems and erect solitary stems with the flower-heads about an inch across. In the West Indies the leaves are used to make medicinal tea for colds.

Erigeron bonariensis

Vernonia cinerea

Elephantopus scaber

143

FAMILY CAMPANULACEAE. This is a small but interesting family in which the flowers are tubular with inferior ovaries. It differs from *Rubiaceae* in having alternate leaves without stipules, and in having latex. The flower parts are in fives, except the carpels, which are often only two in number. The fruit is usually a capsule. The stamens in this family are attached to the corolla and fit closely together so that as a rule only a long-tongued insect can reach the nectar. The flower may be regular or irregular: those with irregular corollas are sometimes put in a separate family, *Lobeliaceae*. Only a few genera are tropical.

Sphenoclea. There is only one species of this genus: *Sphenoclea zeylanica*, Sole Plant or Soap Bush (illustrated). This is an erect branched herb growing up to four feet tall in shallow water, in such places as rice fields and drainage trenches. It is found in all warm countries. The flowers are very small and regular. They are massed together in terminal spikes, and are followed by little capsules which open by a little lid falling off. The oblong, hairless leaves, if rubbed in the hands, produce a froth which can be used for washing.

Isotoma. In this curious genus the flowers have immensely long corolla tubes, but very short stalks. The corolla is regular, but the style is bent at the tip. This genus has the most peculiar distribution, the eight known species being found as far apart as Australia, the Society Islands in the Pacific Ocean, and the West Indies. *Isotoma longiflora* (illustrated) has star-shaped white flowers arising from the base of the plant singly. The leaves are elongated, with indented margins, and are hairy. The fruit is a capsule of two carpels, opening by two valves. The plant is said to be poisonous.

Centropogon. This is a tropical American genus with irregular flowers. The tube is bent, and the bent style and stigma, together with the surrounding stamens, project beyond the corolla. *Centropogon cornutus* (illustrated) has attractive bright rose-pink flowers nearly three inches long. It is a shrubby herb about three feet tall, with shiny leaves. It grows in shady places. The fruit is a capsule.

Sparganophorum
vaillantii

Mikania
micrantha

Eupatorium odoratum

Tridax
procumbans

Ageratum
conyzoides

145

Centropogon cornutus

Sphenoclea zeylanica

Isotoma longiflora

146

FLOWERS OF MONOCOTYLEDON FAMILIES

One seed leaf

Leaf Veins usually parallel

Flower parts often in threes

Plants very seldom woody

Veins of the stems scattered in cross section

FAMILY TYPHACEAE, Reed Mace family. These are tall marsh herbs with strap-shaped, two-ranked leaves, coming from a submerged rhizome. The flowers, which are minute, and have no perianth, are in cylindrical spikes, female below and male above. The single carpel in each female flower becomes a nutlet surrounded by hairs, by which it is dispersed. There is only one genus, **Typha,** Reed Mace, often wrongly termed 'Bull Rush'. The true Bull Rush, *Cyperus*, belongs to the family *Cyperaceae*. There are twelve species, all very much alike, and found by lakesides and swamps all over the world. *Typha australis* (illustrated) is an African species.

FAMILY ALISMATACEAE, Water Plantain family. In this family, which has only eleven genera, the plants have all their leaves from the base, and the leaves may be of more than one kind, some being strap-shaped and submerged, some rounded and floating, and others on erect leaf stalks standing out of the water. They are all water or marsh plants, and usually have white flowers. The flowers have three green sepals and three petals, stamens in multiples of three, and usually many carpels. Each carpel contains one seed, and is free from the others, the 'fruit' being composed of a cluster of these achenes.

Sagittaria, Arrow-head. So-called from the arrow-shaped leaf blades in the aerial leaves of several species. Others have spoon-shaped or oblong erect leaves as well as slender submerged ones. The flowers are generally of two kinds: male ones without carpels but with numerous stamens; and female ones without stamens but with numerous carpels. The petals are usually white. The flowers are in branched inflorescences, the branches being arranged in whorls. The achenes are small and compressed. All the members of the genus except one are American. *Sagittaria pugioniformis* (illustrated) is a native of tropical America. In this species there are a number of male flowers to one female flower, and all the leaves are narrow.

Echinodorus. This genus resembles *Sagittaria* except that all the flowers are complete, and the fruits come to prickly points. There are American and African species. *Echinodorus muricatus* (illustrated) is a tall white-flowered herb of lakesides and fresh

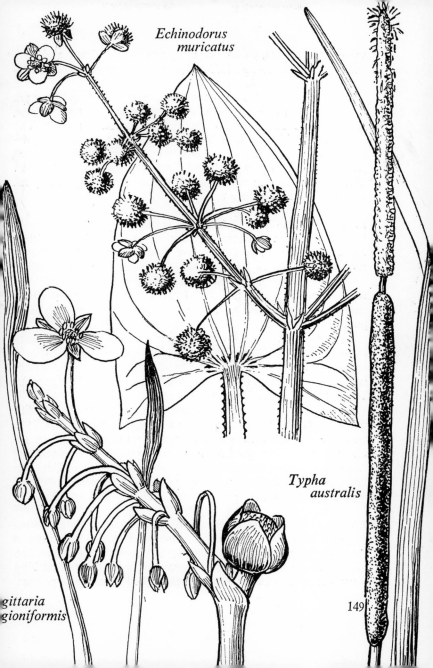

Echinodorus muricatus

Typha australis

*gittaria
gioniformis*

149

water trenches. In this species the stems are ridged, and bear raised, blunt processes. The margin of the leaf stalk is similarly armed.

Lophotocarpus. There are two species of this genus. They are small herbs of shallow fresh water, with leaves of two kinds, strap-shaped submerged ones and oval floating ones. The flowers are white, in umbels. *Lophotocarpus guayanensis* (illustrated) is a common weed of rice fields. It has a yellow spot at the base of each white petal, and there are eight or nine stamens. The carpels are numerous, and flattened, with rough margins. Some of the flowers are unisexual.

FAMILY BUTOMACEAE. This family is very like the last, but the free carpels contain numerous ovules. When ripe they become follicles. The flowers are usually coloured, yellow or pink, and have their parts in threes. The carpels are fewer than in the last family. The inflorescence is an umbel, or the flowers may be solitary. All are marsh or water plants with fleshy rhizomes. There are only four genera, and seven species altogether.

Tenagocharis. There is only one species in this genus, *Tenagocharis latifolia* (illustrated), found throughout the Old World tropics in swampy places. The petals, which fall quickly, are smaller than the sepals. There are nine stamens and six carpels. The leaves are broadly lance-shaped.

Hydrocleys. In this genus, which is native to the West Indies and tropical America, the flowers are large and handsome, the three large petals being much bigger than the sepals. There are numerous stamens and six carpels. *Hydrocleys commersonii* (illustrated) has pale yellow flowers rather like water lilies. The leaves, which are large and spoon-shaped, are erect, not floating. In some places this plant chokes shallow water areas.

FAMILY CYPERACEAE, the Sedge family. This is distinguished from the Grass family (*Gramineae*), which is omitted in this book, by the usually three-sided stem without swollen joints. The leaves are not two-ranked, and their sheathing bases are usually entire, not split and rolled round as in grasses.

150

*Lophotocarpus
guayanensis*

*Hydrocleys
commersonii*

*Tenagocharis
latifolia*

151

In contradistinction to the Grass family, the Sedge family is of little economic value. Most of its members are inhabitants of poor, ill-drained soil, and are of no use for grazing. The flowers of Sedges, like those of Grasses, are without petals and sepals. They are arranged in little inflorescences called spikelets, which are grouped together into larger inflorescences. Each spikelet usually contains several flowers, in the axils of horny bracts called glumes. Sometimes they are unisexual, but in most genera they are hermaphrodite. There are usually three stamens, and two or three united carpels, the ovary containing one ovule, and producing a small nut. There are numerous genera of sedges, many being found nearly all over the world. Most of the tropical genera are common to all warm countries. The determination of species is often the work of experts, but the genera can usually be discerned by means of a hand lens. Only the best known genera of tropical sedges are given here.

Eleocharis, Club Rush. There are many species, often covering wide areas of marshy ground or swamps. The plants have green stems, each ending in a solitary spikelet, and usually no leaves. The flowers are hermaphrodite. The fruit is contracted suddenly at the top of the ovary to form the style, and the base of the style may be swollen. *Eleocharis mutata* (illustrated) is found in both Old and New Worlds. It grows about a foot tall, the stems being erect and sharply three-sided. In many species the stem is cylindrical.

Rhynchospora, Beaked Sedge. In this genus the spikelets are like those of *Eleocharis* but are in heads or panicles, not solitary. The flowers have tiny bristles below, and the three lowest scales of each spikelet have no flowers in their axils. There are numerous species. *Rhynchospora cyperoides* (illustrated) has the spikelets aggregated in small round heads in a branched inflorescence. It is a common swamp species in Africa and America, growing several feet tall.

Fuirena. In this genus each flower has little scales beneath. The spikelets are arranged in branched inflorescences. The stem bears well developed leaves. *Fuirena umbellata* (illustrated) has winged stems and softly hairy leaves and inflorescence. The

152

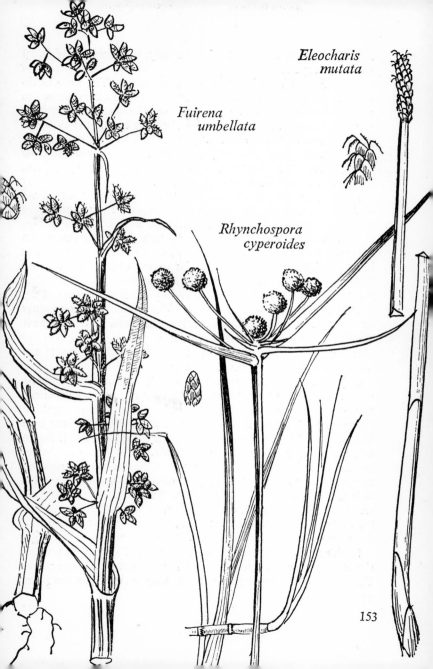

Eleocharis mutata

Fuirena umbellata

Rhynchospora cyperoides

153

lower leaves are reduced to sheaths only. It is very common all over the tropics.

Fimbristylis. This is a very common genus. The flowers do not have scales or hairs beneath. In the spikelets the glumes are arranged on more than one plane. On the nut the style base passes abruptly to the ovary, and the style eventually falls off. As the fruits ripen and fall, the glumes fall, leaving bare stalks. The inflorescence is usually branched. *Fimbristylis miliacea* (illustrated) is a common species in damp grassy places, especially on the margins of rice fields.

Bulbostylis. This genus resembles the last, but the style base remains on the nut, making a little knob. Many species are common on damp savannahs, often in hilly country. *Bulbostylis juncoides* (illustrated) is a common species of American savannahs. It has slender grass-like leaves and spikelets in close heads with a few long bract leaves below. (The specific name 'juncoides' means 'like a Rush'. Rushes are similar-looking plants belonging to a different family, and distinguished by having scale-like perianth leaves. The Rush family is only represented in a few places on tropical mountains; otherwise it is a family of the Temperate regions.)

In the next group of genera the glumes of the spikelets are arranged in two rows, on one plane.

Cyperus. This is the genus from which the family receives its name. There are many handsome species, some cultivated. *Cyperus papyrus* was used by the ancient Egyptians for making Papyrus, which was used like paper. The stems were cut into thin slices and overlapped to make a fair-sized sheet. Some other species are used for rush-work. This genus is distinguished by the style being three-branched, and the spikelet stems remaining on the plant after the fruits and glumes have fallen. *Cyperus rotundus*, Nut Grass (illustrated), is a pernicious weed of cultivated land, especially where the soil is heavy. The narrow underground rhizome produces numerous tubers which are very difficult to eradicate from the ground.

Mariscus. This genus has spikelets like *Cyperus*, but when the fruit is ripe the stalk of the spikelet falls off in one piece. The plants are stout-stemmed with many leaves from the base.

154

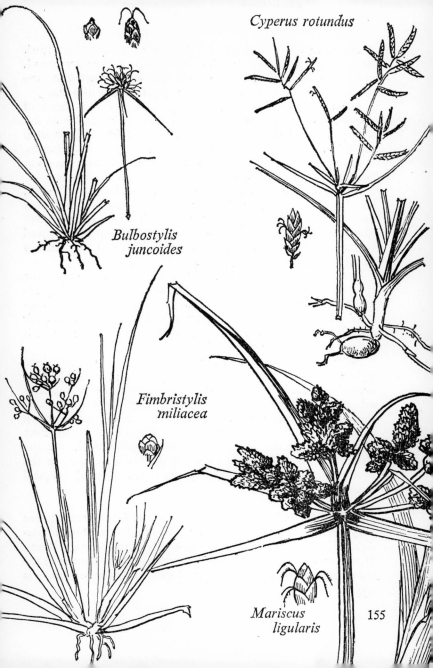

Cyperus rotundus

Bulbostylis juncoides

Fimbristylis miliacea

Mariscus ligularis

155

Mariscus ligularis, Tropical Sea Sedge (illustrated), has a thick stem, surrounded by a few leaf-like bracts, and rather broad, greyish green leaves from the base. The leaves have fine saw-edged margin. It is common in many places near the sea.

Torulinum. In this sedge the spikelets are like those of *Cyperus*, but when the fruit develops the individual nuts fall with joints of the spikelet stem. *Torulinum ferax* (illustrated) has a branched umbel of spikelets surrounded by leafy bracts. It grows about three feet tall, and is common in such places as the margins of rice fields. The stem is sharply triangular.

Kyllinga. In this genus the spikelets are like those of *Cyperus*, but the style has only two branches, and the spikelets have only one or two flowers. *Kyllinga pumila*, Three Leaved Sedge (illustrated), is a common grass-like weed of damp lawns and waysides both in Africa and America. The spikelets form a small head surrounded by long ray-like bract leaves.

Pycraeus. This genus rather resembles *Torulinum*, but the spikelets have flowers with only two style branches. The spikelets have several flowers. *Pycraeus odoratus* (=*Pycraeus polystachyus*) (illustrated) is a common ricefield weed with leafy umbels of spikelets, the leafy bracts being up to a foot long. It is found in all warm countries.

Scleria, Razor Grass. In this genus the nut is supported on an outgrowth of the flower axis. The male and female flowers are in separate spikelets, in spikes or panicles. Several species are semi-climbing in bushy places, forming impenetrable thickets; the leaves have finely serrate cutting edges which can slash the skin. *Scleria pterota* (illustrated) is an erect plant in which the young fruits are purplish-black, but the ripe ones are white. It is common in swampy places in the South American tropics. The genus is found in all tropical countries.

FAMILY ARACEAE, the Arum family. At first glance it is not very obvious that all the plants of this family are Monocotyledons, for their leaves appear to be net-veined in many cases. However, they have the usual scattered vascular bundles in the stem, and they do not become woody. The whole family is

156

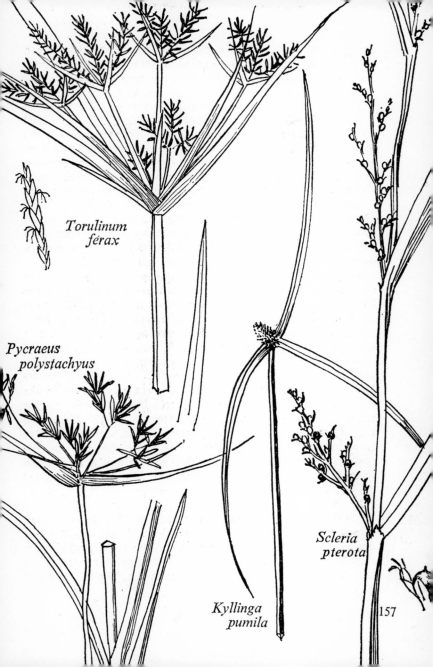

Torulinum ferax

Pycraeus polystachyus

Scleria pterota

Kyllinga pumila

157

easily recognized by the peculiar inflorescence, which is a fleshy spike, or *Spadix*, surrounded at the base by a leafy bract known as the spathe. The plants are rather fleshy herbs and shrubs, nearly all of which are tropical. Very few genera are found all over the tropics. The chief centres of distribution in the tropics seem to be South America, Africa, and South-East Asia. Many have, however, become favourite garden and house plants, and so have been introduced to other areas. Some have attractive leaves, and others attractive inflorescences, but in a number of genera the inflorescence has a very unpleasant smell like bad meat or bad fish, so that it attracts pollinating flies. Naturally this kind of plant is in less demand for cultivation! The most famous of these is *Amorphophallus*, species of which occur in many parts of the Old World tropics. It is recorded that *Amorphophallus titanum*, which grows in Sumatra, produces an evil-scented spadix six feet tall, surrounded by an equally impressive frilled spathe, the whole arising from a starchy corm which may be five feet across. In this genus the leaves come up at a different time from the flowers. They are arrow-head shaped. The genus **Sauromatum**, Monarch of the East, also produces evil-scented flowers before the leaves. The leaves are unique in being cymosely branched. *Sauromatum guttatum* is illustrated opposite. Its large inflorescence has a spotted spathe and a long fleshy spadix.

The large fleshy corms of several genera are eaten in the tropics. When raw they are poisonous, but cooking disperses the poisonous principle. The best known of these edible aroid corms is that of *Colocasia esculentum*, Taro, Coco, or Eddoe (illustrated). In this plant the leaves are peltate (i.e. the leaf stalk arises from about the middle of the blade) and heart-shaped, growing three or four feet tall, from a large rounded cylindrical corm. Rather small inflorescences arise from amongst the leaves at the base, and remain below the leaves. The spadix bears male flowers above, each male flower having its anthers joined together, and female ones below. The top part of the spadix is bare, and tapers to a point. The spathe is long and narrow, being drawn out to a point at the top, and surrounding the spadix. It is much longer than the spadix. The inflorescence

158

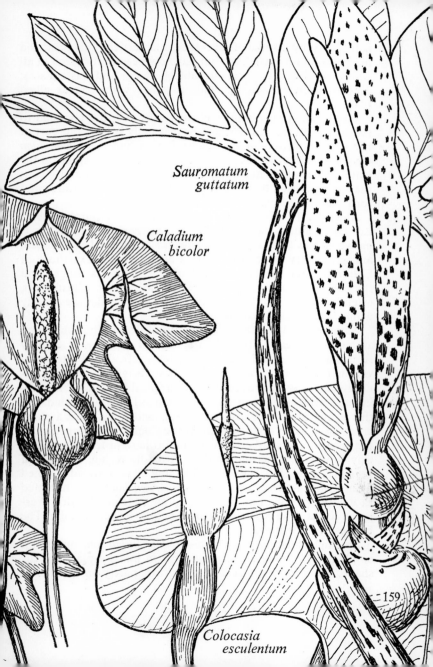

Sauromatum
guttatum

Caladium
bicolor

Colocasia
esculentum

159

is followed by a spike of several-seeded berries. This plant is a native of South-East Asia, but has now been naturalized in all warm countries. It appears in rubbish dumps and waste places, especially on marshy ground, together with several allied plants.

Caladium. A very similar genus to the last, but confined to the American tropics. The spathe is usually broad, and part of the female portion of the spadix is attached to it. *Caladium bicolor* (illustrated) has pretty coloured veins and spots on the leaves. The spathe and spadix are cream-coloured and green; they are followed by whitish berries. Many highly ornamental forms are in cultivation, some of which are hybrids.

Alocasia. This is another genus from which starchy tubers can be obtained, especially *Alocasia macrorhiza*. The genus is native to the East Indies. The leaves are arrowhead-shaped, and grow very large. The flowers are unisexual like those of *Colocasia*, but the barren part of the spadix is longer and thicker. *Alocasia macrorhiza*, Elephant's Foot (illustrated), often has variegated leaves. The spathe and spadix are creamy white. The berries have few seeds.

Anthurium. This is the largest genus of the family, containing about a quarter of its known species. The genus is entirely American but several species have been introduced into cultivation for their attractive leaves and brightly coloured inflorescences. Some are epiphytes in tropical forests, with climbing and attaching green roots, like some kinds of Orchids. In this genus the leaves are net-veined, and arise from a short creeping stem. In their axils are borne single inflorescences with flat spathes and spadices which are fertile right to the top. The tiny flowers are hermaphrodite. After flowering, a spike of berries is produced, each berry hanging by two threads formed from a much-altered perianth. *Anthurium hookeri* (illustrated in colour, p. 135, Fig. 3) is an epiphyte from the dry evergreen forest. The rosette of simple oblong leaves is fleshy. The berries are bright red.

Spathiphyllum. This genus resembles *Anthurium*, but is not epiphytic. The plants generally grow in marshy places in the shade. The spathe is leaf-like, and grows partly up the side of

*Monstera
pertusa*

*Alocasia
macrorhiza*

*athiphyllum
cannifolium*

161

the spadix. This genus does not have attractive berries like those of Anthurium. *Spathiphyllum cannifolium* is illustrated.

Monstera. In this genus the leaves are net-veined, and develop holes as they enlarge. The outermost row of holes may break down to give a pinnate margin. The flowers are naked and hermaphrodite on a thick spadix which afterwards produces a mass of berries. The fruit of *Monstera deliciosa* is edible. The genus is native to the American tropics, the plants being high climbers in forests. *Monstera pertusa* (illustrated) has creamy white flowers and fruits.

Philodendron. This is a large American genus of epiphytic plants, often with creeping stems. Many are favourite house plants ('Tropical Ivy'). The leaves have parallel veins. The spadix bears unisexual, naked flowers, the stamens being stuck together and the ovaries separate. The spathe is erect and thick, and sheaths the spadix. It is swollen at the base. *Philodendron laciniatum* (illustrated) is a climbing species with divided leaves. The cream coloured inflorescence is dark crimson outside the spathe.

Aglaonema. This genus is native to South East Asia. It resembles *Philodendron* in having parallel-veined leaves, and in the spadix of unisexual flowers being surrounded by an erect spathe, but it is a land plant, not an epiphyte, and the inflorescences grow in succession like a one-sided cyme. *Aglaonema commutatum* (illustrated) is a native of Malaya. It has yellow spathes and large orange-red fruits.

Dieffenbachia. In this American genus the stem is thick and erect, bearing oblong leaves. Most members of the genus are marsh plants. The spathe is cylindrical, not swollen below, and is rolled round the long spadix which projects beyond the top of the spathe. The flowers are unisexual, the female ones below having flat, cushion-like stigmas, and the male flowers being closely aggregated towards the top. *Dieffenbachia sequine,* Dumb Cane (illustrated), is so called because the leaves contain a poison which numbs the tongue for several days if they are bitten. In the West Indies it is said to have been used as a torture for slaves. The spathe is green, the spadix cream, and the berries orange.

Philodendron laciniatum

Pistia stratiotes

Aglaonema commutatum

163

Two other interesting genera are worth mentioning. *Pistia stratiotes*, the Water Lettuce (illustrated), is the only member of a curious genus of floating plants with reduced stems and a rosette of pale green, parallel-veined leaves. The inflorescence is of the typical aroid form, but is very minute. Reproduction is largely by means of side shoots or runners. This plant is found in all warm countries. The other genus consists of only two species of plants confined to South America, *Montrichardia*. These plants are immense, thick-stemmed herbs which clothe the banks of the lower reaches of many of the rivers, and are useful in preventing erosion. The plants form a forest of stems up to twenty feet tall, with shiny arrowhead-shaped leaves and yellow inflorescences. The fruiting stem looks like a curious pineapple; the puffy fruits eventually falling off and floating away. *Montrichardia arborescens*, Mucka-mucka, is illustrated.

FAMILY XYRIDACEAE. This is a small tropical family of sedge-like herbs with narrow sheathing leaves from the base. They are tufted annuals or perennials, some growing in rather acid wet ground, and others in rather saline swamps. There are only two genera. The flowers are in close heads, in the axils of overlapping leathery bracts. They are irregular, with three sepals, and a united corolla of three petals. The three carpels are united to form a single ovary and style, with three separate stigmas. The fruit is a capsule with numerous seeds. The only widely distributed genus is **Xyris**. In this genus the flowers are yellow, with three stamens opposite the petals. The two lateral sepals are boat-shaped, and the third one is hooded, protecting the corolla. *Xyris jupicai*, Yellow-eyed Grass (illustrated in colour, p. 136, Fig. 1), is one of the larger tropical American species. It grows to the height of about four feet. The stem is slightly flattened and winged.

FAMILY ERIOCAULACEAE. In this small family the plants are small, tufted herbs with small heads of tiny white flowers and narrow grass-like leaves. The flowers are regular and uni-sexual. The sepals are chaff-like and free; the petals form a little cup, and the whole head has bracts surrounding it. The genera

Montrichardia
arborescens

Dieffenbachia
sequine

165

number only nine, of which the largest are **Eriocaulon,** Pipe wort, in which the stamens are double the number of petals, **Paepalanthus,** in which the stamens equal the number of petals, and **Syngonanthus,** in which the petals of the female flower are joined in the middle. It is very difficult for anyone except an expert to distinguish the genera and species. Several species of *Paepalanthus* and *Syngonanthus,* which are common on sandy savannahs in the American tropics, are called Pincushion Plants. They also occur in Africa. *Syngonanthus umbellatus* (illustrated) has heads of white flowers on stalks up to six inches long, the main stem below the umbel being about the same height, and springing from a rosette of narrow, hairy leaves.

FAMILY FLAGELLARIACEAE. This is another very small family, with only three genera. It consists of plants with stout stems, sometimes climbing, with long leaves, parallel veined, and sheathing at the base, and sometimes ending in a tendril. The flowers are in terminal panicles; they are not very showy, but small and clustered together. Each has three sepals and three petals, six stamens, and a superior ovary of three carpels which later produces a berry with three seeds. The genus **Flagellaria** is found all over the Old World tropics. There are four species. They are climbers, with the tip of the leaf forming a tendril. *Flagellaria guineensis* (illustrated) is a fairly common high climber along river banks in tropical Africa.

FAMILY COMMELINACEAE. This family fairly closely resembles the last, but the flowers are showy (usually blue or purple), and the family includes hardly any climbers. In this family the stem appears jointed, the sheath of the leaf, as in the last family, being closed to form a tube. The flowers have green sepals and quite large coloured petals, which are free as a rule, and clawed at the base. There may be six stamens, or only three, the other three being functionless outgrowths. The fruit is nearly always a capsule.

Commelina. In this genus the inflorescence is partially enclosed by a spathe-like bract. The flowers have two or three stamens, and are generally blue. *Commelina nudiflora*

Flagellaria guineensis

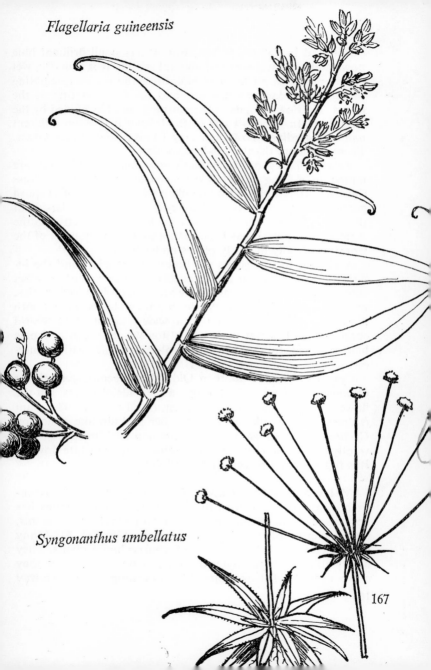

Syngonanthus umbellatus

167

(illustrated in colour, p. 135, Fig. 4) has small brilliant blue flowers arising in the axil of an oval spathe. It is found in wet grassy places in all tropical countries, the leaves resembling those of a broad-leaved grass, and the stem rooting at the nodes. The flowers open in the morning, and have faded by the afternoon. In various parts of the tropics it is given different names, including Zeb Grass, Day Flower, and Water Grass. There are more than a hundred species.

Zebrina. This genus resembles *Commelina*, but the petals are united in a long tube. *Zebrina pendula*, Cockroach Grass (illustrated), is a pretty trailing plant with its leaves of purplish green marked with two bands of pale green. The underside of the leaf is purple, and the flower is also purple. Native to the American tropics, it has been naturalized in many parts of the world, especially in shady places under trees.

Aneilema. In this genus the flower is irregular, and the inflorescence is terminal and branched, at the end of an erect stem with grass-like leaves. There are about a hundred species, mostly natives of the Old World, but they also occur in South America. *Aneilema sinicum* is a widely spread Old World species, found in wet places. The flowers are green and pale lilac-coloured, followed by three-valved capsules with numerous seeds.

Cyanotis. This is another Old World genus, resembling *Commelina* in having the flowers in the axils of bracts, but the flowers have all the stamens perfect, or all but one. The plant is erect, from a tuft, or with a tuber or bulb-like structure. *Cyanotis lanata* (illustrated) is a common African species with woolly leaves and clusters of pale blue, pink, or white flowers. It is found in wet places, often on hilly ground.

FAMILY BROMELIACEAE. This interesting family is entirely confined to America in its origins. Only one genus has been dispersed to all other parts of the tropics: *Ananas comosus*, the Pineapple (illustrated in colour, p. 136, Fig. 5). Many other members of the family are favourite house plants. They nearly all grow as epiphytes on trees, or on rocks, where they make a rosette of thick, pointed leaves arranged in such a way

168

Zebrina
pendula

Cyanotis
lanata

169

that they form a cavity in the centre of the plant, which holds water. The inflorescence stem arises from this centre. It is usually a branched spike with coloured bracts below the flowers. It is the series of bracts in most cases which form the attractive part. The fruit is a berry or a capsule with, as a rule, hairy seeds. These plants are some of the most characteristic inhabitants of the South American tropical forest, more than eight hundred species being known. The family is of little economic importance except that some species yield fibres from their tough leaves and, of course, the Pineapple is of great importance. This plant shows many of the usual features of the family: the tuft of stiff leaves with spiny margins forming a rosette from which a central spike of flowers arises, bearing coloured bracts and regular flowers with inferior ovaries. In this genus, however, the fruit is peculiar in that all the berries coalesce to make a large 'compound' fruit, the axis running through the middle and forming a terminal tuft of leaves. This tuft, when broken off, will take root and give rise to a new plant, a fact which may explain the plant's wide distribution as a semi-wild form, especially in dry, sandy places.

FAMILY LILIACEAE. This family has recently been broken up into a number of smaller ones, the original name of the family being retained for the most typical forms. It is proposed to treat all these various sub-groups as far as they are mentioned in this book under the original family name. This family includes all the true lilies, with a regular perianth of six parts in two whorls, both coloured, six stamens and three united carpels, with a superior ovary. The inflorescence is a simple or branched raceme. Tropical members of the family are widely scattered, mostly in the Old World.

   Chlorophytum. A widely spread genus with branched spikes of white, or white and green, flowers arising from a tuft of leaves which are not fleshy or spiny. There is a short rootstock below the ground, but no bulb. The fruit is a lobed capsule. *Chlorophytum comosum* (illustrated) often produces tufts of leaves at the end of the flowering stem, which bends down so that they root in the soil. A form with variegated leaves is often cultivated.

Smilax cumanensis

Asparagus plumosus

Chlorophytum comosum

171

Asparagus. This is an Old World genus in which the leaves have been reduced to minute scales, and their place taken by flattened green, leaf-like branches called cladodes. The plants have very small creamy-white flowers, followed by red or black berries. In some species the stem is a semi-twining climber, clinging by hooked prickles (the modified bases of scale leaves). Others, including the species which yields edible shoots, *Asparagus officinalis*, have erect stems. All are perennials, sending new shoots each season from a base with fleshy roots, and they are most common in dry areas. The Asparagus 'fern', *Asparagus plumosus* (illustrated), is a native of Zanzibar. The small green cladodes are very numerous, arranged in flat sprays which are frequently used with cut flowers.

Smilax. This genus is sometimes placed in another family, *Smilacaceae*. It is widely distributed in bushy places in both hemispheres. The plants are climbers with alternately arranged, broad leaves. The leaves bear paired tendrils at the base, and the stem generally has hooked prickles. The fleshy root of several South American species yields sarsaparilla. The flowers are like those of *Asparagus*. They are green or white, and are grouped in umbels. The fruit is a red or black berry. *Smilax cumanensis* (illustrated) is a common South American species of bushy places. The small greenish flowers are followed by bluish fruits.

Gloriosa. This is a genus of climbing lilies with leaf tendrils like those of *Flagellaria*. The herbaceous climbing stem arises from an underground fleshy rootstock. There are five species, natives of Asia and Africa, but introduced as garden plants to all tropical countries. The best known species, *Gloriosa superba*, is illustrated in colour, p. 135, Fig. 1. In this species the perianth leaves are much fluted and waved, and the leaves are in whorls of three. It is common in bushy places in tropical Africa and Asia.

Sansevieria. This is a genus of about sixty species with thick underground rhizomes and tough, fleshy leaves containing fibres (Bow-string Hemp). The flowers have the usual lily form, with slender greenish white perianth leaves; they are borne on a slender spike, and are followed by orange or red berries.

172

*Cordyline
terminalis*

*Sansevieria
thyrsiflora*

173

Sansevieria thyrsiflora, Bow-string Hemp, Mother-in-Law's Tongue (illustrated), is a native of Africa which has been naturalized in America and parts of tropical Asia. The leaves in this species are mottled and blotched with lighter and darker green.

Cordyline. This genus, together with the Dragon's Blood Tree (**Dracaena**) and the last genus, are often placed in a separate family from *Liliaceae*. In the genus **Cordyline** the plant is rather woody, but generally less so than *Dracaena*. Most species are natives of the eastern Old World. The flowers are in terminal branched spikes; the flowers have a united perianth. *Cordyline terminalis*, Surveyor's Plant (illustrated), has a woody stem about twelve feet tall, with long, lance-shaped leaves at the top of the rather slender branches. It produces creamy-white panicles of flowers, but numerous varieties are grown in gardens for their coloured leaves, forms being known with bright pink or red variegation. As these are very conspicuous, the stems are often stuck in as boundary marks, and soon take root. The plant is a native of Asia and Australia.

AMARYLLIDACEAE. This family has the same characteristics as the previous family except that the ovary is inferior. Like *Liliaceae* the family contains many bulbous plants, and some woody ones resembling palms (*Agave*, etc.). Most members of the family belong to the temperate or sub-tropical regions.

Crinum. This is the largest tropical genus, and is found all over the tropics. The plants are bulbous, with all the leaves from the base, and a showy inflorescence arises on a thick stem in the axil of one of the thickened leaf bases. The flowers are large and nearly regular, with all parts in multiples of three. They usually have no individual stalk, but arise in the axils of sheathing bracts at the top of the main inflorescence axis. The perianth leaves are united, with the stamens attached to them. Many live in sandy places by the sea or along river banks, where the large seeds, which have a corky exterior, are dispersed by water. *Crinum commelyni*, Spider Lily (illustrated), is common along the banks of South American rivers. The flowers are white.

174

Crinum
commelyni

Haemanthus
tenuiflorus

175

Haemanthus. In this genus a very large number of small flowers with long stamens arise from a kind of umbel. The flowers are red or pink, and appear before the leaves. The genus contains about seventy species, all African, but some have been introduced to other parts as garden flowers. *Haemanthus tenuiflorus*, Painter's Brush Lily (illustrated), has pale red flowers and rather broad leaves arising from the bulb when the flowers are over. The leaves are spotted with purple at the base.

Hymenocallis. An American genus which has been introduced to other parts and has run wild in Africa. In this genus the flower has a cup (corona) uniting the bases of the filaments of the stamens. The fruit, which grows into a large capsule, never has more than six seeds. *Hymenocallis tubiflora* (illustrated) has white flowers with slender perianth lobes. The perianth tube is immensely long and slender, but the individual flowers have no stalks. The leaves are rather broadly lanceolate.

Zephyranthes. A genus of small lilies originating in Central America which have been naturalized in grassy places in many hot countries, where they are variously known as 'crocus', 'snowdrop', and Thunder Lily, the latter in allusion to the fact that the flowers spring up immediately after the first heavy rains. The flowers arise singly from small bulbs, and are followed by three-valved capsules with black seeds. The leaves are slender and grass-like. *Zephyranthes eggersiana* (illustrated) has bright yellow flowers an inch or more long, and does superficially resemble a true crocus. Other species are pink, and white.

Curculigo. This, and the allied genus **Hypoxis,** are sometimes placed in a special family, *Hypoxidaceae*. They are low growing plants with tufts of narrow, grass-like leaves arising from a fleshy corm or rhizome below the ground. The flowers are star-like and bright yellow with a long perianth tube, and they generally appear before the leaves with the first rains on the savannahs. *Curculigo scorzonerifolia*, Savannah Lily, Savannah Star, Pig Food (illustrated), owes its last name to the fact that its stout elongated corm is rooted out and eaten by pigs.

FAMILY PONTEDERIACEAE. This is a small family of water plants with showy blue or mauve flowers, which are regular

*Hymènocallis
tubiflora*

*Curculigo
scorzonerifolia*

*Zephyranthes
eggersiana*

177

with a superior ovary, and are arranged in racemes protected by a sheathing leaf at the base. The fruit is a capsule.

Eichornia, Water Hyacinth. In this genus the six perianth segments are united to form a tube below. The flower has six stamens. The upper leaves at least are rounded or spoon-shaped, and stalked. *Eichornia crassipes* (illustrated in colour, p. 136, Fig. 4), originating in America, has become a widely spread pest in tropical waterways, choking ditches and canals. The plant floats, supported by the swollen hollow bases of the leaves, and increases rapidly by runners till the whole water surface is covered.

Heteranthera. In this genus the normal flowers have only three stamens, and some have only one. The genus occurs in Africa and America. In some the leaves are all alike; in others, including *Heteranthera reniformis* (illustrated), the leaves are of two kinds, floating and submerged. The flowers are pale blue.

VELLOZIACEAE. This is a very small family resembling *Amaryllidaceae*, except for certain details of structure of the ovary, and the fact that in one genus there are numerous stamens instead of six. They also have a peculiar, repeatedly forked branching, and tufts of hard, pointed leaves at the ends of the branches, the leaves having serrated margins. The stems are really quite slender, but they are thickly clothed by the remains of dead roots, which collect water like a sponge, and allow the plants to live in rocky places where the water supply is very irregular. **Vellozia** occurs all over some savannahs in Africa and South America. The flowers are showy and produced singly. They are white. *Vellozia maudeana* (illustrated) is a South American species. The small, tree-like plants grow about two feet tall.

TACCACEAE. Another very small family, but with wide distribution. There are only two genera, **Tacca,** which produces berries, and **Schizocarpa,** which has capsule fruits. The plants have creeping rhizomes with branched leaves on long stalks, and umbels of flowers like those of *Amaryllidaceae* except that the capsule has no partition. *Tacca parkeri* (illustrated) has

178

Tacca parkeri

Vellozia maudeana

Heteranthera reniformis

179

purplish flowers and purplish berry fruits. *Tacca pinnatifida* yields East Indian Arrowroot.

FAMILY IRIDACEAE. This interesting family is represented in the tropics by a number of isolated genera none of which has a very wide distribution. The chief centres of distribution are South Africa and tropical America. Plants of this family are easily recognized by their usually regular flowers with showy coloured perianths united below into a narrow tube, and only three stamens. There are three united carpels, forming an inferior ovary, a single style, and three, usually petal-like or flattened stigmas. The fruit is a capsule. Many of the family have two-ranked sheathing leaves flattened from side to side. A large number of genera are confined to tropical mountains, or inhabit the temperate regions.

Gladiolus. In this genus the flower is irregular, and borne in a terminal spike. The seeds are winged. There are about two hundred and fifty species of these plants, all natives of the Old World, mostly from Africa. *Gladiolus primulinus* (illustrated) is a native of the African savannahs which has been hybridized to give a large range of colours. The wild species has clear yellow flowers with the upper perianth leaf forming a hood. All Gladioli grow from corms, and several species reproduce themselves readily from seed.

Sisyrinchium. This mainly American genus is represented by about seventy savannah plants, all growing from short rhizomes, with two-ranked laterally flattened leaves. The flowers are yellow, white, or blue, borne in branched inflorescences, several flowers springing from one spathe. The style-branches are entire. *Sisyrinchium alatum* (illustrated) is a yellow-flowered form which grows about a foot high.

Belamcanda. This is a pretty genus from Eastern Asia, with spreading apricot-salmon coloured flowers with dark spots, borne in forked inflorescences. The capsule produces a number of shiny black seeds, which has given this plant the common name of Blackberry Lily. There is only one species, *Belamcanda chinensis* (illustrated in colour, p. 135, Fig. 5).

Cipura. This is a West Indian genus with petaloid stigmas,

180

Cipura
martinicensis

Gladiolus
primulinus

Sisyrinchium
alatum

181

the plant growing from a corm. *Cipura martinicensis* is a plant about a foot high, with yellow and dark brown flowers. It grows in damp, grassy places.

FAMILY DIOSCOREACEAE, the Yam family. Wild yams are common in bushy places and forests all over the tropics. The twining stem springs from a large, swollen tuber which contains much starch, and is cultivated in all hot countries. **Dioscorea,** Yam, has over six hundred species. In this genus the leaves are alternate, and usually heart-shaped. They are net-veined. The flowers are small and green, with a bell-shaped perianth with six lobes, six stamens, and three joined carpels, which have three styles or a three-lobed style, and an inferior ovary. The fruit is a three-winged capsule, with winged seeds. Some of the species contain a poisonous principle which is used by the South American Indians as an arrow poison and as a fish poison. They also contain a substance used in the manufacture of the drug Cortisone. *Dioscorea trifida,* Cush-cush Yam (illustrated), is a species with edible tubers which also produces an arrow poison.

FAMILY MUSACEAE, the Banana family. No one knows exactly where the cultivated banana, and its close relatives the Plantain, and Manilla Hemp, first hailed from, as they are now cultivated all over the tropics. The wild members of the same genus **Musa,** however, are found in the Old World. They are huge herbs with false 'stems' made by the overlapping leaf bases. The huge inflorescence, which has 'hands' of female flowers and ends in the male part of the inflorescence protected by huge bracts, dies after the fruit has developed, and a new shoot comes up from a huge rhizome underground. To this family also belong two Traveller's Palms (**Ravenala** and **Phenakospermum)** occurring respectively in Madagascar and British Guiana. There are four other genera. The largest is **Heliconia,** all species of which are natives of tropical America. These plants have rhizomes and large entire leaves like bananas, but the leaves are in two ranks, and the flowers are in cymes, in the axils of coloured bracts, and the fruit is not fleshy, but separates into

182

Hedychium coronarium

Dioscorea trifida

Renealmia exsaltata

183

three hard portions. *Heliconia psittacorum*, a marsh plant growing about three feet tall, is illustrated in colour, p. 136, Fig. 2.

CANNACEAE. Only one genus is found in this family, the Canna Lily or Indian Shot. *Canna indica* is found all over the tropics. The plants have rhizomes from which arise erect stems bearing broad, sheathing leaves and terminal inflorescences of scarlet or yellow flowers of peculiar shape. The flowers have three erect sepals and three showy petals, joined below to form a tube. Only one stamen is fertile, and this is shaped and coloured like a petal, with the anther down one side. The other stamens are also altered; three or four are transformed to 'petals', one, called the labellum, being larger than the rest. The other two or three stamens are functionless. The three carpels are united, and have a petal-like style. The ovary is inferior, and turns into a three-valved capsule with blunt prickles all over, which contains a large number of round seeds resembling shot. *Canna coccinea* is illustrated in colour, p. 136, Fig. 3. Cultivated Cannas are hybrids, mostly derived from *Canna indica*.

ZINGIBERACEAE. This family resembles the last in consisting of plants with fleshy rhizomes. It includes several plants of economic importance; *Zingiber officinale* is Ginger, **Curcuma** yields Indian Arrowroot and Turmeric, **Amomum** yields Cardamon. From *Alpinia galanga* is obtained Siamese Ginger. These products are obtained from the rhizome, which contains aromatic oils. Plants of this family have rather broad, grass-like leaves with sheathing bases, and often a ligule where the sheath joins the blade. The flowers are in racemes, heads, or cymes; they are at least as complicated as those of *Canna*, but the labellum is lobed, and is formed by the union of two stamens. One stamen is fertile, and two others may be transformed to petals. The fruit is a capsule.

Costus. This large genus is found throughout the tropics. The flowers are in dense heads, protected by large scale-like bracts. The labellum is very large, but the petals and sepals are quite small. The ovary is three-celled. *Costus cylindricus*, a South

184

Thalia
geniculata

Maranta
arundinacea

Calathea
cyclophora

185

American species growing in damp forests, is illustrated in colour, p. 135, Fig. 2.

Hedychium. There are about fifty species of this genus, mostly from Asia. In this genus the large flowers have broad labellums which are two-lobed. The stamen filament is long. The spike has several flowers. *Hedychium coronarium*, Ginger Lily, has large strongly-scented flowers. It is a native of India, but has been naturalized in many other parts, including the New World tropics.

Renealmia. In this genus the plants have tall, cane-like shoots. The flowers either arise on separate stems from the leaves or are on leafy stems. The inflorescence is many-flowered. The fruit is a berry. There are no petals derived from the lateral stamens, which are absent. The genus occurs both in West Africa and in America. *Renealmia exsaltata* (illustrated) has tall leafy stems up to eight feet high, and short inflorescences of yellow flowers followed by rose-red berries.

FAMILY MARANTACEAE, West Indian Arrowroot family. In this family the flowers rather resemble those of *Canna* and *Zingiberaceae*, but are usually rather small. The leaves are two-ranked, and there is a stalk between the blade and the sheath. The plants grow from fleshy rhizomes. The leaf blade is usually broad, with the veins diverging from a central one. The flowers are in spikes or panicles, with bracts beneath. Most plants of this family live in forest swamps.

Thalia. This is the only genus of the family found in both Old and New Worlds. It is a tall herb of the waterside, with much-branched panicles of rather small mauve-blue flowers. The leaves are equal sided. There are seven species. *Thalia geniculata* is illustrated.

Maranta. Many species in this genus have pretty markings on their leaves, and are grown as ornamental plants. *Maranta arundinacea*, West Indian Arrowroot (illustrated), resembles *Thalia geniculata*, but has white flowers. This is an American genus.

Calathea. This is also an American genus. The flowers are in spikes or heads with large, cup-like, often coloured bracts in

186

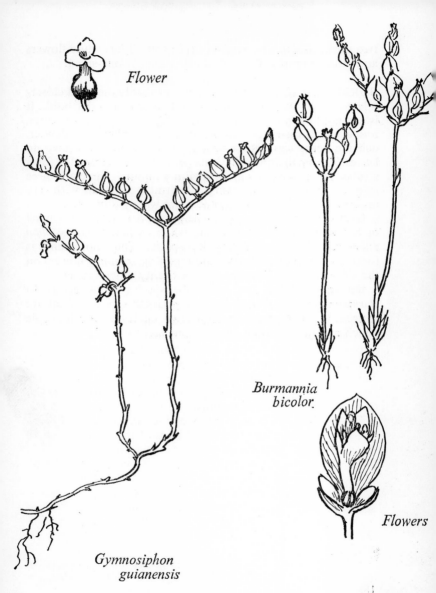

Flower

*Burmannia
bicolor*

Flowers

*Gymnosiphon
guianensis*

two ranks. *Calathea cyclophora* (illustrated) has white flowers and pinkish bracts. The leaf blade is slightly one-sided.

BURMANNIACEAE. This family is probably the most closely related to the Orchids, which are not described in this book. It is a small family of plants, many living as forest saprophytes, found widely distributed in the tropics. The plants are slender, delicate herbs less than a foot high, some of which have no leaves. The small flowers have six perianth leaves joined to form a tube. The inner lobes are sometimes minute. There are three stamens, and an inferior ovary. The fruit is a capsule with very numerous, tiny seeds. Two genera are widely dispersed.

Gymnosiphon. In this genus the perianth tube is not winged or boat-shaped. The flowers are white or blue. *Gymnosiphon guianensis* (illustrated) is a typical species. The inflorescence is forked, with a central flower and regularly arranged flowers on the side branches. There are about twenty other species.

Burmannia. There are about forty species in this genus. In *Burmannia bicolor* (illustrated) the perianth tube and fruit are winged, the winged part being in two shades of bluish purple which contrast with the golden stamens.

HINTS ON COLLECTING AND PRESERVING PLANTS

If the reader wants to learn the names of many plants he cannot find in this or other books, the best way is to collect them and preserve them in such a way that they can be identified. The local Agricultural Department or the Forestry Department may have an herbarium which can be consulted, or the specimens may be sent to a museum or university. The Royal Botanic Gardens, Kew, Richmond, Surrey, England, has the largest collection of living and dried plants in the world, and is pleased to receive specimens and to determine their names.

The plants to be preserved should be fresh, not dying or withered, and they should be collected in dry weather if possible. They are placed between sheets of special thick, absorbent paper, sold for the purpose by biological supply houses. Ordinary blotting paper is too thin and soft to be satisfactory. Successive layers of paper and plant specimens are placed on top of each other and placed between drying presses. These are firm metal frames filled in with wire netting. Pressure is now exerted by straps, which are tightened as the specimens dry and shrink. The paper will need changing every day and replacing with dry paper, but the sheets can be used again and again. As soon as the plants are stiff and dry they must be preserved from insects and moulds, either by dipping in, or by brushing with a 2 per cent solution of Mercuric Chloride in Alcohol. In some plants all the leaves tend to fall off in drying. This may be stopped by dipping the stems quickly in and out of boiling water before pressing. Do not immerse the flowers. Plants which remain alive cannot be dried, and with very resistant plants the covering sheet of paper may be sprayed with formalin 40 per cent. This kills the plant and prevents it going mouldy while drying. Next time the paper is changed, the sheet which is damp with formalin can be removed. Notes should be made of the original colour and form of the flower, habit of the plant, pollination, environment, etc., and every specimen must be clearly numbered and duplicated for reference. In every case put the date and place where found. Collect several specimens of each, with leaves and fruit where possible, but do not collect so many that you seriously deplete the plant in its natural habitat. Specimens to be sent away for naming should not be mounted, but should be packed between sheets of newspaper, the parcel being protected by stout cardboard.

Specimens may be mounted on sheets of white paper 17×11 in (this is the standard size). They are best kept in place by strips of gummed paper. Sticky cellulose tape is *not* suitable; in the tropics it deteriorates and discolours in a very short time, and loses its adhesive power. Sheets of preserved specimens can be kept in stiff brown paper folders, and stored in a dry cupboard free from cockroaches, termites, rats and mice.

A SHORT GLOSSARY OF BOTANICAL TERMS
USED IN THIS BOOK

Many of the following terms are explained in more detail in the chapter on Plant Classification, and some are explained as they occur in the text, but they are all put here for convenience of reference.

Achene. A dry, one-seeded fruit which does not open to set free the seed.
Anterior (of a flower). The side away from the main inflorescence stem.
Anther. The head of a stamen. It produces pollen.
Aril. A fleshy outgrowth on a seed.
Axil. The angle between a leaf and the stem.
Axis. The main direction of growth of the plant. Main axis is the main stem.
Bract. A leaf, often coloured or reduced to a scale, beneath a flower.
Bracteole. A smaller leaf, like a bract, above a bract or at the side of it, on the flower stem.
Capsule. A dry dehiscent fruit of more than one carpel.
Carpel. The female organ of the flower. Each carpel has a swollen part, the Ovary, below, and a sensitive Stigma at the top. There is usually a lengthened part, the Style, between. Carpels may be united, either at the ovary, or completely so that their number is not immediately obvious.
Compound Leaf. A leaf in which the blade or lamina is completely divided into separate leaflets.
Connective. The part of the stamen which joins the anther to the filament. It often bears outgrowths.
Corolla. The petals.
Corona. Outgrowths of the petals resembling an extra corolla.
Corymb. A raceme in which the lower flowers have much longer stalks.
Cotyledons. The first leaves of a seedling. The embryo in the seed of a Dicotyledon contains two Cotyledons, whereas that of a Monocotyledon contains only one.
Cyme. An inflorescence in which each main axis ends in a flower.
Dehiscent (of a fruit). Opening to let out the seeds.
Drupe. A fleshy fruit in which the innermost wall is a hard, woody 'stone'.
Epiphyte. A plant which grows on another plant but which is not parasitic on it, e.g. many Orchids and Aroids.
Filament. The stalk of a stamen.
Follicle. A dehiscent fruit formed from one carpel and opening down one side only.
Glume. A hard, horny bract characteristic of the Grass and Sedge families.
Gynophore. An outgrowth of the receptacle carrying the ovary up on a stalk, as in *Gynandropsis* and *Passiflora.*
Herb. Herbaceous plant. A plant which does not become very woody like a shrub or tree.
Inferior Ovary. The ovary of a flower in which the receptacle has grown up round it so that the other flower parts appear to arise on top of it, as in Pumpkin.

191

Inflorescence. The arrangement of flowers on a stem.

Legume. A fruit formed from one carpel which dehisces into two valves.

Ligule. A membranous strip between the sheath and the blade of the leaf, characteristic of the Grass and Ginger families.

Lomentum. An indehiscent dry fruit which has one-seeded portions arranged end to end.

Naked (of flowers). Having no perianth.

Net-veined (of leaves). Having the veins branched to form a net-work.

Nut. A one-seeded indehiscent dry fruit formed from two or more carpels.

Nutlet. The dry, indehiscent fruitlet of the families *Boraginaceae* and *Labiatae* (like achene, but derived from originally joined carpels).

Ovary. The part of the carpel which contains ovules.

Ovules. The structures containing the egg cells. After fertilization they become seeds.

Palmate. Having leaf veins or leaflets radiating from a common point.

Pedicel. A flower stalk in an inflorescence which has more than one flower.

Peduncle. The main stem of an inflorescence.

Perianth. The one or two outer whorls of floral leaves (sepals and petals).

Petal. A member of the inner whorl of perianth leaves. It may be absent.

Petiole. A leaf stalk.

Pinnate. Having a main vein with lateral veins branching from it, or having a main rachis with a row of leaflets on each side.

Pinnule. One part of a compound leaflet.

Pollen. Single, thick-walled cells produced in the anther, which later give rise to male nuclei.

Raceme. An inflorescence in which all the flowers arise as lateral branches.

Rachis. The midrib of a compound leaf.

Receptacle. The swollen end of the flower stalk, which bears the floral leaves.

Rhizome. An underground stem which grows horizontally. It often contains stored food.

Schizocarp. A separating fruit.

Sepal. A member of the outermost whorl of perianth leaves.

Serrate. Saw-edged (of leaf margin).

Siliqua. A long capsule of two carpels, divided down the centre by a 'false' septum or partition, and dehiscing from below upwards.

Spadix. A thick, fleshy spike.

Spathe. A large leafy bract sheathing an inflorescence.

Spathulate. Spoon-shaped.

Spike. An inflorescence of the raceme type in which the individual flowers have no stalks.

Stamen. A male organ of the flower.

Stipules. Paired outgrowths from the base of a leaf.

Superior Ovary. The ovary of a flower in which the carpels and the axis are not sunk in the receptacle.

Tendril. A climbing organ, usually coiled, but sometimes claw-like.

Torus. A receptacle.

Trifoliate (of compound leaves). Composed of three leaflets.

Umbel. An inflorescence in which all the flowers are stalked, and arise at the top of a stout peduncle called a scape.

Valvate. Having sepals or petals which meet in bud but do not overlap.

INDEX OF SCIENTIFIC NAMES

(Numbers in bold type refer to genera which are illustrated)

195

196

INDEX OF POPULAR NAMES

198

199